REFERENCE BOOKS

FOR THE

HISTORIAN OF SCIENCE

for Cecil

with best wishes

SAJ 1.3.82

Science Museum Library

Occasional Publications 2

Also in this series:
A Catalogue of Books Printed Before 1641
in the Science Museum Library
Compiled by Judit Brody
(1979)

REFERENCE BOOKS FOR THE HISTORIAN OF SCIENCE

A HANDLIST

Compiled by

S. A. JAYAWARDENE

SCIENCE MUSEUM
LONDON
1982

Science Museum
South Kensington, London SW7 2DD

First Published 1982

British Library Cataloguing in Publication Data

Jayawardene, S.A.
Reference books for the historian of science.
(Occasional publications/Science Museum Library,
ISSN 0262-4818; 2)

1. Science–History–Bibliography
2. Reference Books
I. Title
016.509 Z7405.H6
ISBN 0-901805-14-9

Printed in Great Britain by
Hobbs the Printers Limited
Southampton

PREFACE

This *Handlist* is the result of a bibliographical exercise, undertaken by me some years ago in the belief that the historian of science needs a handy list of reference books to help him with the problems he meets with in his work. While there are many excellent bibliographical manuals which cover the primary and secondary sources of the history of science, there are very few which include the *general reference books* which the historian of science frequently needs in the course of his studies. (One of the best guides for the historian of science, Ferguson's *Bibliography of the history of technology*[1], contains about 140 out of some one thousand titles listed by me.) In compiling this list I have had in mind the companion-guide which I wish I had owned when I was a research student. The requirements of both student and scholar have been taken into account, while, at the same time, trying to restrict the work to a manageable size. A large number of reference books of use to the historian of science which would have qualified for inclusion in a larger work, have been left out. It is hoped that they can be found with the help of the bibliographical guides listed here. Some entries have been annotated. Comments from users of the *Handlist* are welcome.

When compiling this list I made frequent use of the bibliographical guides of Sarton, Ferguson, Malclès, Walford, and Winchell.[2] During the early stages of planning the work I profited a great deal from reading Gino Loria's two papers on a proposed research manual for the historian of mathematics,[3] as well as from a study of Malclès' *Manuel de bibliographie.*[4] I have also benefited from many long hours spent browsing in libraries, both here and abroad, particularly in the Bodleian, the British Library, the Cambridge University Library, the University of London Library, the City Library of Bologna, and the Vatican Library. Furthermore, my employment for seventeen years on the staff of the Science Museum Library has given me the unique opportunity of scanning a variety of library journals, scientific periodicals, and bibliographical works, and, most important of all, of observing the historian of science at work.

S.A.J.
January 1982.

[1] No. 12 in *Handlist.*

[2] Nos. 3, 12, 680, 682, 687 in *Handlist.*

[3] "Sur les moyens pour faciliter et diriger les études sur l'histoire des mathématiques", *Atti del IV Congresso Internazionale dei Matematici, Roma, 6–11 Aprile 1908* (Rome, 1909), vol. 3, pp. 541-548. (Also published in *Archiv für Geschichte der Naturwissenschaften und der Technik*, 1 (1960), 9-18).
"Développements relatifs au projet d'un 'Manuel pour les recherches sur l'histoire des mathématiques'". *Bibliotheca mathematica*, (3), 9 (1908), 227-236.

[4] No. 686 in *Handlist.*

CONTENTS

Part II. History and Related Subjects

Part III. General Reference

Indexes

ACKNOWLEDGEMENTS

Many friends and colleagues criticized the draft of this work at different stages – from the viewpoint of specialists, librarians and future users. Ivor Grattan-Guinness read through the list and suggested several additions. Colleagues in the Library helped me to arrange the titles, prepare the indexes, and check the proofs.

With the project invading our home, my wife and son willingly accepted the inevitable dislocations of domestic life and actively helped me with scissors and paste, and with typing and checking the indexes. Wendy Sheridan read through the draft typescript and first proofs, and pointed out many errors and inconsistencies of style. Anne Jack (of Department 6, Science Museum) patiently prepared camera-ready copy on an IBM Composer and cheerfully coped with numerous last-minute additions and amendments (which could not have been made if conventional methods of publication had been used). My thanks go to all of them, and, not least, to John Chaldecott, former Keeper of the Library, who encouraged me and obtained official approval for the project which I had begun as a hobby.

S.A.J.

INTRODUCTION

The *Handlist* consists of some one thousand titles arranged in 44 chapters. The whole work is divided into three parts. Part I relates to the history and literature of science (from students' guides to lists of historians of science); part II deals with history in general (from manuals of research to historical dictionaires); and part III contains general reference books (from bibliographical guides to style manuals). The list does not pretend to offer the historian of science a ready answer to every problem. Instead, it aims at providing him with a wide range of tools to help him solve them.

A code number has been given to each entry. The numbers run consecutively from the first to the last entry and are intended only as a finding device. However, there has been a certain amount of pre-publication revision: some entries have been removed and new ones added. Hence the irregularities of sequence and the presence of letters added to the code numbers.[1] Sufficient bibliographical information has been given in each entry to enable the work to be identified; in certain cases, notes have been added describing the contents and citing critical reviews.[2]

Periodicals (serials) have been given open entries, that is, with "+" placed after the year of publication and the volume number (if any). In the case of directories published annually, the latest copy seen by me has been listed; but open entries have been given where it was thought that the whole run would be useful. Works published in parts are indicated by the words "*In progress*" added after the description.

Titles which merit special attention from students starting research are marked by an asterisk placed after the code number.[3] It would be worth pointing out (at the risk of stating the obvious) that many a bibliographical problem could be solved with the aid of the guides to reference books listed in chapters I and XXXI.[4]

LOCATIONS

For the convenience of readers using the Science Museum Library, the locations of several works have been given. A press-mark or the symbol SML at the end of an entry means that a copy of the work is in the Science Museum Library. However, as many new books are on order, it is advisable to check with the library staff before deciding that a work is *not* in the Library. In the case of some encyclopedias and directories which are not in the Science Museum Library, other convenient locations have been given: Warburg Institute, Victoria and Albert Museum Library (VAL), Lyon Playfair Library (LPL), and British Museum (Natural History) Library.

INDEXES

There are two indexes – author/title and subject. Arrangement is word-by-word. References are to the code numbers given in the *Handlist* and not to the pages. When indexing duplicate entries in the list (there are a few), the second code number has been placed in parentheses, preceded by "=".

Author/Title index

This contains entries for authors and for short-titles of works. There are also entries for editors, but not in the case of works which are well known by their titles. Entries for principal authors are followed by the short-titles of the respective works.

Subject index

In compiling the subject index every effort has been made to indicate the main subjects covered by the works in the *Handlist* in so far as they relate to the history of science and technology and to the needs of the student/researcher. There are entries for disciplines, topics, regions and time-periods. Where necessary, the same work has been entered under more than one heading. Entries have been made for the different categories of reference material (bibliographies, dictionaries, abstracts, etc.) in the list. Library catalogues have also been entered in one alphabetical sequence under: *Library catalogues – 'by city'*. As general reference works cover a variety of subject fields it is impractical to index their contents systematically. However, topics of special interest, which have received extensive treatment in certain manuals, have been indexed, and, in exceptional cases, the relevant page-numbers indicated.

Prepositions and articles at the beginning of subheadings have been ignored in determining the alphabetical order of subheadings. **Bold** type has been used for main headings, and also to emphasize the most important references (code numbers) in an entry.

see cross-references have been made from unused (synonymous) forms of heading to those actually used, and from broader headings to specific ones. In some cases there are *see* cross-references made from specific to broader headings (e.g., history of mathematics *see* mathematics). This was done where it seemed useful to assemble related subjects under a common heading.

see also cross-references have been made from broader headings to more specific headings and also between related headings. Their purpose is to show where additional relevant information can be found.

see under and *see also under* do not actually refer to the named heading but to one of its subheadings.

above and *below* in cross-references indicate that the reference is to another subheading under the same heading, and not to a separate heading.

S.A.J.

[1] Although the manuscript was completed in April 1980 many works published since then have been added. A few entries had to be shortened in order to make room for additional titles. Some were added after the indexes had been typed. (Item 555B is not in the author/title index and items 711A and 766 have not been indexed at all.)

[2] Words in quotes in the annotations have been taken from the prefatory material in the book or from the cited review.

[3] Nos. 3, 4, 12, 21, 23, 24, 78, 81, 224, 673, 680, 681, 682, 687, 851, 852, 854, 882, 883, 954, 963.

[4] The works of Malclès (680, 686), Walford (682), Winchell/ Sheehy (687) and Higgens (687A) are particularly recommended for the annotations of the reference books listed. Many of the works in the present *Handlist* are described in them in detail.

Part I

The History of Science and its Sources

[1 – 302A]

I. GUIDES TO THE STUDY OF THE HISTORY OF SCIENCE

1. *Bibliographies of Bibliographies*

NEU (John) The history of science. *Library trends,* 15 (1967), 776-792. [Survey of bibliographies of books and articles on the history of science and technology (including bibliographical guides) by the present editor of the *Isis* Critical Bibliography] (016:93:5) [1]

2. *History of Science*

SARTON (G.) The study of the history of science. Cambridge: Harvard Univ. Pr., 1936. 75 pp. [Text of inaugural lecture delivered at Harvard University, with a short bibliography. Complements 7] (016:93:5) [2]

SARTON (G.) Horus. A guide to the history of science. A first guide for the study of the history of science with introductory essays on science and tradition. Waltham, Mass.: Chronica Botanica, 1952. 316 pp. [Student's manual, written towards the end of Sarton's career, *Horus* is the offspring of the journals *Isis* (1912–) and *Osiris* (1936–68) which he founded. Part I consists of three essays based on the History of Science Lectures delivered at University College London in 1948. Part II is an introductory bibliography based on Sarton's own library. Although the bibliography needs updating, the chapters on historical methods

(1), atlases (3), gazetteers (4), encyclopaedias (5), biographical collections (6), abstracting and review journals (12), national academies and scientific societies (13), journals and serials concerning the history of science (20), and organization of the study and teaching of the history of science (21–26), are still useful. Of special interest are the introductory notes to each chapter and the informative comments on authors. Book reviews and many articles in *Isis* are noted. Reviews: *Isis*, 44 (1953), 91-93; *Scripta mathematica*, 19 (1953), 256-257; *Journal of documentation*, 9 (1953), 70-72] (016:93:5 and 5:93) [3]*

RUSSO (F.) Éléments de bibliographie de l'histoire des sciences et des techniques. 2e éd. Paris: Hermann, 1969. 214 pp. [Essential reference book for the historian of science, whatever his speciality. More extensive and more detailed than *Horus* (3): for comparison, *see* Russo's note on p. 13. Includes the history of technology. Lists *primary sources and related studies.* Many items annotated. Secondary sources include articles in periodicals. For many works, the press-marks of copies in the Bibliothèque Nationale (or another Parisian library) are given. Many book reviews noted] (016:93:5) [4]*

BLACK (Sandra) *and* THOMSON (Ron B.) History and philosophy of science: a guide to study and research at Oxford University. 2nd ed. Oxford, 1973. 40 pp. (016:93:5) [5]

LORCH (R.P.) Aids to research in the history of science. Manchester: UMIST, 1977. 13 pp. (016:93:5) [6]

UNIVERSITY OF PENNSYLVANIA LIBRARY. Special bibliography: history of science, medicine and technology. Compiled by E.T. Morman. Philadelphia, 1979. 36 pp. [Brief annotations] (016:93:5) [6A]

CORSI (Pietro) *and* WEINDLING (P.), *Eds.* Information

sources for the history of science and medicine. London: Butterworths [*In press.* Series of 22 bibliographical essays, intended to provide a comprehensive up-to-date survey of the discipline, its sources and problems] [6C]

3. History of Mathematics

SARTON (G.) The study of the history of mathematics. Cambridge: Harvard Univ. Pr., 1936. 113 pp. [Text of inaugural lecture delivered at Harvard University, with bibliographical notes. Pp. 67–103: collected works and biographical notices of the leading mathematicians of the 19th and 20th centuries. Complements 2] (016:93:5) [7]

LORIA (G.) Guida allo studio della storia delle matematiche. 2nd ed. Milan: Hoepli, 1946. 385 pp. [Written for students, this introductory manual offers the bibliographical expertise acquired by Loria during his 60 years as mathematician, historian, teacher and editor. In 12 chapters, some 1,600 titles are enumerated and commented upon (Ch. 2: survey of histories of mathematics; Ch. 3: analysis of the contents of the principal journals for the history of mathematics). Much of Ch. 5-7 is of interest to *all* historians of science. A more comprehensive work was originally planned (*Atti del IV Congresso internazionale dei matematici*, Rome, 1909, vol. 3, pp. 541-548), but not realized. A useful complement to Loria's guide is: Felix Müller, *Führer durch die mathematischen Literatur mit besonderer Berücksichtigung der historisch wichtigen Schriften*, Abhandlungen zur Geschichte der mathematischen Wissenschaften, 27 (Leipzig: Teubner, 1909; 252 pp.)] (016:93:51) [8]

4. History of Physics

BRUSH (S.G.) Resources for the history of physics. Hanover: Univ. Pr. of New England, 1972. 176 pp. (016:93:53) [9]

5. *History of Biology*

BOURDIER (F.), LEGÉE (G.), GUÉDÈS (M.), THÉODORIDES (J.) *and* LASSIUS (Y.) Introduction bibliographique à l'histoire de la biologie. *Histoire et nature,* 3-4 (1974–1975): 1-195. [Companion-guide to all aspects of research in the subject. *See also* 34] (016:93:57 *and* 93JH5226) [10]

6. *History of Medicine*

ARTELT (W.) Einführung in die Medizinhistorik, ihr Wesen, ihre Arbeitweise und ihre Hilfsmittel. Stuttgart: Enke, 1949. 240 pp. [Review: *Bulletin of the history of medicine,* 26 (1952), 489-491] (61:93) [11]

7. *History of Technology*

FERGUSON (E.S.) Bibliography of the history of technology. Cambridge, Mass.: Society for the History of Technology, 1968. 347 pp. [Excellent vade-mecum for the student, covering every aspect of the subject. Extensively annotated bibliographies in 14 chapters (some 1,700 items under 60 headings). Pp. 1-171 useful to historians of *all* sciences. Each chapter has a brief introduction] (016:93:6) [12]*

INDUSTRIAL ARCHAEOLOGIST'S GUIDE 1971–1973. Newton Abbot: David and Charles, 1971. 201 pp. (016:93:6) [13]

PANNELL (J.P.M.) The techniques of industrial archaeology. 2nd ed. Edited by J. Kenneth Major. Newton Abbot: David and Charles, 1974. 200 pp. (6:93) [14]

HUDSON (Kenneth) A pocket book for industrial archaeologists. London: John Baker, 1976. 134 pp. (6:93) [15]

II. BIBLIOGRAPHIES OF THE HISTORY OF SCIENCE

1. *History of Science*
2. *History of Science in Antiquity*
3. *History of Islamic Science*
4. *History of Mathematics*
5. *History of Cartography*
6. *History of Geology*
7. *History of Biology*
8. *History of Medicine*
9. *History of Technology*

1. *History of Science*

RIDER (K.J.) History of science and technology: a select bibliography for students. 2nd ed. London: Library Assn., 1970. 75 pp. (016:93:5) [16]

SARTON (G.) Introduction to the history of science. Baltimore: Williams and Wilkins, 1927–48. 3 vol. in 5. (Carnegie Instn. publ. 376). [Provides a framework for the study of science and thought in classical antiquity and the Middle Ages. Each chapter/part deals with a time period, varying from two centuries to half a century, and contains: a survey of science and learning; notes on religion, philosophy and culture; bio-bibliographical notes on the leading personalities. Indexes] (5:93) [17]

JOHN CRERAR LIBRARY, CHICAGO. A list of books on the history of science, January 1911. Prepared by Aksel G.S. Josephson. Chicago, 1911. Supplements 1-2. 1917–45. (017:93:5) [18-20]

BIBLIOGRAPHIE ANALYTIQUE DES PUBLICATIONS RELATIVES A L'HISTOIRE DE LA SCIENCE (*afterwards* Critical bibliography of the history of science and its cultural influences), 1912+. In *Isis*: revue consacrée à l'histoire de la science. Wondelgem-lez-Gand, Belgium, (Washington, D.C.) 1913+. [Annual since 1954. Classified bibliography of books and periodical literature. Not strictly critical, but analytical, with occasional notes. Begun in 1912 as Sarton's personal index, it is today the standard current bibliography for the history of science. Encyclopedic in scope, but from the view-point of the historian of *science*. Historians of special sciences have to supplement it with other sources: see *Isis*, 47 (1956), 250-251. Mainly confined to literature in West-European languages. Two World Wars, reliance on scholars sending offprints, and the frequent turn-over of collaborators contributed to irregularities in coverage, especially in languages other than English and French. Classification is chronological, ethnographical and systematic, but preference is given to the first two. No item is entered under more than one heading. (Classification scheme modified in 1955 on Sarton's retirement.) Book reviews noted (separate list from 1968). Some 600 periodicals examined systematically in 1979. For cumulations *see* 24, 24A] (93JI94) [21] *

MIELI (A.) Bibliografia metodica dei lavori di storia della scienza in Italia. *Archeion:* Archivio di storia della scienza, 1 (1919–20), 84-86, 195-217, 332-356, 397-420; 5 (1924), 163-175, 284-298; 6 (1925), 159-168, 347-359; 7 (1926), 152-176, 411-413; 8 (1927), 274-287; 10 (1929), 36-39. [*Not continued*] (93JA793) [22]

BULLETIN SIGNALÉTIQUE. 22. Histoire des sciences et des techniques. Paris: C.N.R.S., 1961+ [From 1952 to 1960: *Bulletin analytique.* Quarterly. Current bibliography of articles and book reviews, arranged by subject and period. Brief notes. Annual cumulated subject and author indexes. Wide coverage (some 2,000 journals scanned in 1976–78)] (016:5) [23] *

ISIS CUMULATIVE BIBLIOGRAPHY. A bibliography of the history of science formed from ISIS Critical Bibliographies 1-90, 1913–65. Edited by Magda Whitrow. London: Mansell, 1971–76. [The result of weeding, tidying and sorting the *Isis* Critical Bibliographies 1-90. Vol. 1-2: Personalities and Institutions; Vol. 3: Subjects (without reference to a particular period or civilisation). Vol. 4 and 5 (*in press*) deal with history of science of a particular period or civilisation. See *Isis*, 70 (1979), 160-163] (016:93:5) [24]*

ISIS CUMULATIVE BIBLIOGRAPHY 1966–1975. A bibliography of the history of science formed from ISIS Critical Bibliographies 91-100. Edited by John Neu. London: Mansell, 1979. [Vol. 1: Personalities and institutions. 1979. Vol. 2 *in preparation*] (016:93:5) [24A]

LOPEZ PIÑERO (J.M.) PESET REIG (M.) *and* GARCÍA BALLESTER (L.) Bibliografía histórica sobre la ciencia y la técnica en España. Valencia: Cátedra e Instituto de Historia de la Medicina, 1968–73. 2 vol. (Cuadernos hispanicos de historia de la medicina y de la ciencia, 7, 13). (016:93:5) [24B]

COMITÉ BELGE D'HISTOIRE DES SCIENCES. Notes bibliographiques. Répertoire cumulatif, séries 1 à 71, 1946–1968. Brussels: Éditions Culture et Civilisation, 1970. 207 pp. (016:93:5) [25]

FISHER (N.W.) *and* BROCK (W.H.) A list of Ph.D. theses in the history of science and related areas in British universities, 1945–74. *British journal for the history of science,* 8 (1975), 267-278. (93JB749) [26]

2. *History of Science in Antiquity*

FORBES (R.J.) Bibliographia antiqua: philosophia naturalis. Leyden: Nederlandsch Instituut voor het Nabije Oosten, 1940–50. 1 vol. in 10 pts. suppl. 1-2. 1952–63. (016:93:5) [27]

3. History of Islamic Science

MIELI (A.) La science arabe et son rôle dans l'évolution scientifique mondiale. Réimpression anastatique augmentée d'une bibliographie avec index analytique par A. M. Mazahéri. Leyden: Brill, 1966. 467 pp. [Originally published 1938] (5(5):93) [28]

NASR (S.H.) An annotated bibliography of Islamic science. Tehran: Imperial Iranian Academy of Philosophy, 1975–78. 2 vol. [*In progress.* Review (Vol. 1): *Isis*, 69 (1978), 457-461] (016:93:5(=927)). [29]

4. History of Mathematics

MAY (K.O.) Bibliography and research manual of the history of mathematics. Toronto: Univ. of Toronto Pr., 1973. 818 pp. [A "first approximation to a complete bibliography" of secondary sources. Based on five serial bibliographies. Weak on the literature before 1868 and on Oriental studies. Review: *Isis*, 65 (1974), 524-526] (016:93:51) [30]

HISTORIA MATHEMATICA, Vol. 1+ Toronto, 1973+ [Quarterly. Contains abstracts of current literature. Annual index of authors of works reviewed and abstracted] (93JH5229) [31]

ROGERS (Leo) Finding out in the history of mathematics: a resource file of bibliographic, audio-visual and other materials for students and teachers. Leicester: Leapfrogs, 1979. 50 pp. [Restricted to works (in English) easily available through libraries. Partly annotated] (016:93:51) [32]

DAUBEN (J.W.), *Ed.* Annotated bibliography in the history of mathematics. New York: Garland Press [*In press.* Contributions from 53 specialists. In six sections: general reference works; source material; general histories of mathematics: histories of mathematics — chronological, by subject; selected topics] [32A]

5. History of Cartography

RISTOW (W.W.) Guide to the history of cartography: an annotated list of references on the history of maps and map-making. Washington, D.C.: Library of Congress, Geography and Map Division, 1973. 96 pp. [33]

6. History of Geology

SARGEANT (William A.S.) Geologists and the history of geology: an international bibliography from the origins to 1978. London: Macmillan, 1980. 5 vol. [Review: *History of science,* 19 (1981), 224-226] (016:93:55) [33A]

7. History of Biology

SMIT (Pieter) History of the life sciences. An annotated bibliography. Amsterdam: Asher, 1974. 1071 pp. [Some 3,000 works (120 bibliographies; 1,500 histories of biological sciences; 450 histories of medicine; 60 biographical dictionaries; 850 biographies) classified under 130 headings. Annotations include references to less important works. Complements Bourdier's guide (10)] (016:93:57) [34]

8. History of Medicine

ARTELT (W.) Index zur Geschichte der Medizin, Naturwissenschaft und Technik. Munich: Urban and Schwarzenberg, 1953–66. 2 vol. [Covers the period 1945–1951/52] (016:93:5) [35]

WELLCOME HISTORICAL MEDICAL LIBRARY [*now* Wellcome Institute for the History of Medicine]. Current work in the history of medicine, no. 1+ London, 1954+ [Quarterly] (016:61) [36]

NATIONAL LIBRARY OF MEDICINE, BETHESDA, Md. Bibliography of the history of medicine, no. 1+ Bethesda, Md., 1965+ [Annual] (016:93:61) [37]

JOURNAL OF THE HISTORY OF MEDICINE AND ALLIED SCIENCES. Cumulative index, vol. 1-30, 1946–1975. Prepared by Manfred Waserman and Carol T. Clausen. New Haven, Conn., 1977. 131 pp. (93JJ886) [38]

LINDEBOOM (G.A.) A classified bibliography of the history of Dutch medicine, 1900–1974. The Hague: Nijhoff, 1975. 663 pp. (016:93:61) [39]

9. History of Technology

JOHN CRERAR LIBRARY, CHICAGO. A list of books on the history of industry and industrial arts. January 1915. Prepared by Aksel G.S. Josephson. Chicago, 1915. 486 pp. (017:93:6) [40]

COOPER UNION LIBRARY, NEW YORK. A guide to the literature on the history of engineering. New York, 1946. 50 pp. (017:62:93) [41]

HEPBURN (W.M.) A manual of the William Freeman Myrick Goss Library of the History of Engineering and associated collections. Lafayette: Purdue Univ., 1947. 218 pp. Suppl. 1953. 66 pp. (017:62) [42]

POOLE (M.E.) "History" references from the *Industrial arts index* 1913–1957. Raleigh, N.C., 1958. 119 pp. (016:93:6) [43]

NEWCOMEN SOCIETY FOR THE HISTORY OF ENGINEERING AND TECHNOLOGY. Analytical bibliography of the history of engineering. *Transactions*, 2 (1921/22) –– 22 (1941/42), 25 (1946/47). [*Not continued*] [Subject index in vol. 10 and 20] (93TL6724) [44]

NEWCOMEN SOCIETY FOR THE HISTORY OF ENGINEERING AND TECHNOLOGY. General index to *Transactions*, vol. 1-32, 1920–1960. London, 1962. 111 pp. (93TL6724) [45]

GOODWIN (J.) Current bibliography in the history of technology. *Technology and culture*, 5 (1964)+ [Annual] (93JT3825) [46]

TECHNOLOGY AND CULTURE. Ten year index [1959–1969, vol. 1-10]. Compiled by Barton C. Hacker. Chicago: Univ. of Chicago Pr., 1973. 205 pp. (93JT3825) [47]

SHIERS (George) Bibliography of the history of electronics. Metuchen, N.J.: Scarecrow Pr., 1972. 323 pp. (016:93:621.37) [48]

III. MANUALS

1. *Philosophy. History of Ideas*
2. *Histories of Science, Medicine and Technology*

1. *Philosophy. History of Ideas*

TOTOK (W.) Handbuch der Geschichte der Philosophie. Frankfurt-on-Main: Klostermann, 1964–77. [Vol. 1: Altertum; Vol. 2: Mittelalter; Vol. 3(1): Frühen Neuzeit. *In progress*] [49]

ENCYCLOPEDIA OF PHILOSOPHY. Paul Edwards, editor in chief. New York: Macmillan, 1967. 8 vol. (03) [50]

DICTIONARY OF THE HISTORY OF IDEAS: Studies of selected pivotal ideas. Philip P. Wiener, editor in chief. New York: Scribner's, [1973]. 4 vol. (03) [51]

RICHTER (Joachim) *and* GRÜNDER (K.), *Eds.* Historisches Wörterbuch der Philosophie. Basle: Schwabe, 1971–76. [4 vol. (A–K). *In progress*] [52]

2. *Histories of Science, Medicine and Technology*

DARMSTAEDTER (L.) Handbuch zur Geschichte der Naturwissenschaften und der Technik. 2nd ed. Berlin: Springer, 1908. 1262 pp. [Kraus reprint 1960] (5:93) [53]

DAUMAS (M.), *Ed.* Histoire de la science. Paris: Gallimard, 1957. 1900 pp. (Encyclopédie de la Pléiade) (5:93) [54]

KNIGHT (D.M.) Sources for the history of science, 1660–1914. London: The Sources of History Ltd., 1975. 223 pp. [Study of the use of historical evidence. Surveys the sources under: histories of science; MSS; journals; scientific books; non-scientific books; surviving physical objects. Review: *Isis*, 68 (1977), 299-302] (5:93) [55]

NEEDHAM (Joseph) Science and civilisation in China. Cambridge: Cambridge Univ. Pr., 1954–76. [Vol. 1-5(3). *In progress*] (5(5):93) [56]

ENCYKLOPÄDIE DER MATHEMATISCHEN WISSENSCHAFTEN mit Einschluss ihrer Anwendungen. Leipzig: Teubner, 1898/1904–35. 6 vol. in 23. [Begun by Felix Klein, Heinrich Weber and Franz Meyer. Aims to provide concise and comprehensive coverage of mathematics and its applications, while surveying the literature from 1800. Contributions from three generations of mathematicians. Main index in vol. 4 (1935)] (51) [57]

ENCYCLOPÉDIE DES SCIENCES MATHÉMATIQUES PURES ET APPLIQUÉES. Édition française d'après l'édition allemande. Paris: Gauthier–Villars, 1904–14. 7 vol. in 26. [Details in Russo (4), p. 138. See also *Bibliotheca mathematica*, (3), 14 (1915), 336-340] (51) [58]

NAAS (J.) *and* SCHMIDT (H.L.) Mathematisches Wörterbuch mit Einbeziehung der theoretischen Physik. Berlin: Akademie Verlag, 1961. 2 vol. (413:51) [59]

ARCHIBALD (R.C.) Outline of the history of mathematics. Menasha, Wis.: Mathematical Assn. of America, 1949. 114 pp. (*American mathematical monthly,* vol. 56, suppl.) (51:93) [60]

HERMANN (Armin) Lexikon Geschichte der Physik A–Z. Biographien, Sachwörter, Originalschriften und Sekundärliteratur. Cologne: Deubner, 1972. 423 pp. (53:93) [61]

Manuals

PARTINGTON (J.R.) A history of chemistry. London: Macmillan, 1961–70. 4 vol. [Vol. 1, pt. 2 *not published*] (54:93) [62]

WEYER (J.) Chemiegeschichtsschreibung von Wiegleb (1790) bis Partington (1970): eine Untersuchung über ihre Methoden, Prinzipien und Ziele. Hildesheim: Gerstenberg, 1974. 282 pp. (Arbor scientiarum, Reihe A: Abhandlungen, vol. 3) (54:93) [63]

NEUFELDT (S.) Chronologie Chemie 1800–1970. Weinheim: Verlag Chemie, 1977. 359 pp. (54"18/19":93) [64]

PUSCHMANN (Th.) Handbuch der Geschichte der Medizin. Editors, Max Neuburger and Julius Pagel. Jena: Gustav Fischer, 1902–1905. 3 vol. [Georg Olms reprint 1971] (61:93) [65]

SINGER (Charles), HOLMYARD (E.J.), HALL (A.R.), *and* WILLIAMS (T.I.), *Eds.* A history of technology. London: Oxford Univ. Pr., 1954–78. 7 vol. (6:93) [66]

GILLE (Bertrand), *Ed.* Histoire des techniques. Paris: Gallimard, 1978. 1652 pp. (Encyclopédie de la Pléiade) (6:93) [67]

IV. BIOGRAPHIES OF SCIENTISTS

1. *Indexes to Biographies*
2. *Bio-bibliographies*
3. *Biographical Dictionaries*
4. *Biographical Memoirs of Learned Societies*

1. *Indexes to Biographies*

IRELAND (N.O.) Index to scientists of the world from ancient to modern times: biographies and portraits. Boston, Mass.: Faxon, 1962. 662 pp. [Indexes 338 books published between 1877 and 1961 (some 7,500 scientists)] (92(100)) [68]

PELLETIER (P.A.), *Ed*. Prominent scientists; an index to collective biographies. New York: Neal-Schuman, 1981. 311 pp. [Some 10,000 scientists in English books published between 1960 and 1979. Supplements Ireland (68)] [68A]

BARR (E.S.) An index to biographical fragments in unspecialized scientific journals. University, Ala.: Univ. of Alabama Pr., 1973. 294 pp. [Citations on some 7,700 persons in: *American journal of science* 1890–1920; *Proceedings, Royal Society of Edinburgh* 1832–1920; *Proceedings, Royal Society of London* 1800–1933; *Nature* 1869–1918; *Popular science monthly* 1872–1915; *Science* 1883–1919] (92(100)) [69]

FRUTON (Joseph S.) Selected bibliography of biographical data for the history of biochemistry since 1800. 2nd ed. Philadelphia: American Philosophical Society, 1977. 240 pp. (92:57) [70]

HUNT BOTANICAL LIBRARY. Biographical dictionary of botanists represented in the Hunt Institute portrait collection. Boston: G.K. Hall, 1972. 451 pp. [Index to a collection of 17,000 portraits] (92:57) [71]

BARNHART (J.H.) Biographical notes upon botanists. Boston: G.K. Hall, 1965. 3 vol. [Index of 44,700 cards in the New York Botanical Garden Library] [72]

CARPENTER (Mathilde M.) Bibliography of biographies of entomologists. *The American midland naturalist,* 33 (1945), 1-116; 50 (1953), 257-348. [73]

GILBERT (Pamela) A compendium of the biographical literature on deceased entomologists. London: British Museum (Natural History), 1977. 455 pp. (92:57) [74]

DESMOND (Ray) Dictionary of British and Irish botanists and horticulturists including plant collectors and botanical artists. London: Taylor & Francis, 1977. 764 pp. [Revision of J. Britten and G.E.S. Boulger's *A biographical index of British and Irish botanists* (1931)] (92:57) [75]

NEW YORK ACADEMY OF MEDICINE. Catalog of biographies in the library of the New York Academy of Medicine. Boston, Mass.: G.K. Hall, 1960. 165 pp. [76]

BELL (S.P.) A biographical index of British engineers in the nineteenth century. New York: Garland Publishing, 1975. 246 pp. [Lists some 3,000 engineers] (92:62) [77]

2. Bio-bibliographies

POGGENDORFF (J.C.) Biographisch-literarisches Handwörterbuch (zur Geschichte) der exakten Wissenschaften. Leipzig: Barth; Berlin: Akademie Verlag, 1863–1976. [Bd. 1-7. *In progress.* Title varies. Coverage: Bd. 1-2, to 1857; Bd. 3, 1858–83; Bd. 4, 1883–1904; Bd. 5, 1904–22; Bd. 6, 1923–31; Bd. 7a (German speaking), 1932–53 with suppl. for earlier periods; Bd. 7b (others), Teil 1-5, A-M.

Subjects covered include: biology and medicine (except Bd. 5, 6); history of science (from Bd. 6). Gives for each scientist a brief biographical sketch (indicating *Festschriften,* obituaries) and a list of his books and papers. Weak on pre-1800 scientists. Indispensable for the 19th century] (92(100)) [78]*

FERCHL (Fritz), *Ed.* Chemisch-pharmazeutisches Bio- und Bibliographikon. Im Auftrage der Gesellschaft für Geschichte der Pharmazie. Mittenwald: Nemayer, 1937–38. 2 vol. [Includes notices of pharmacologists, physiologists and chemical technologists not found in Poggendorff] (92:54) [79]

ARCHIBALD (R.C.) Bibliographia de mathematicis. *Scripta mathematica,* 1 (1932–33), 173-181, 265-274, 346-362; 2 (1933–34), 75-85, 181-187, 282-292, 363-373; 3 (1935), 83-92, 179-190, 266-276, 348-354; 4 (1936–37), 82-87, 176-188, 273-282, 317-330. [Bio-bibliographical notices, with index, of some 200 mathematicians, mostly of the twentieth century. Complements Eneström's list of obituary notices of 300 mathematicians, who died between 1881 and 1900, in *Bibliotheca mathematica*, (3), 2 (1901), 326-350] (92:51) [80]

3. Biographical Dictionaries

DICTIONARY OF SCIENTIFIC BIOGRAPHY. Charles Coulston Gillispie, editor-in-chief. New York: Scribner, 1970–80. 16 vol. ["Single most valuable reference work" in the history of science. Bio-bibliographical notices on *c.* 5,000 scientists, from Thales to Bernal. Living scientists not included. Six topical essays in Suppl. I (vol. 15) on Indian, Babylonian, Assyrian, Egyptian, early Japanese and Mayan science. Vol. 16 contains a name and subject index to the biographical articles and bibliographies in vol. 1-15; it includes persons who are not the subjects of biographical articles. There are separate lists of: contributors and biographees; societies; periodicals; scientists (by field). Review: *Isis*, 71 (1980), 633-652] (92(100)) [81] *

MAYERHÖFER (J.) *and others.* Lexikon der Geschichte der Naturwissenschaften: Biographien, Sachwörter und Bibliographien. Vienna: Hollinek, 1959–70 [Vol. 1: Aachen-Dodel. *In progress*] [82]

HIRSCH (A.) Biographisches Lexikon der hervorragenden Ärzte aller Zeiten und Völker. Berlin: Urban, 1929–35. 5 vol., suppl. [83]

EDEN (Peter), *Ed.* Dictionary of land surveyors and local cartographers of Great Britain and Ireland 1550–1850, compiled from a variety of sources. London: Dawson, 1975–76. 3 pt. [84]

WORLD WHO'S WHO IN SCIENCE. Ed., Allen G. Debus. Chicago: Marquis-Who's Who, 1968. 1855 pp. (92) [85]

ELLIOTT (C.A.) Biographical dictionary of American science: the seventeenth through the nineteenth centuries. Westport, Conn.: Greenwood Pr., 1979. 360 pp. (92(73)) [85A]

4. *Biographical Memoirs of Learned Societies*

INSTITUT DE FRANCE. Index biographique de l'Académie des Sciences du 22 décembre 1666 au 1er octobre 1978. Paris: Gauthier-Villars, 1979. 513 pp. (92:5(4/9)) [86]

ROYAL SOCIETY, LONDON. Index to the *Proceedings* of the Royal Society of London (old series), Vol. 1-75, 1800–1905. London: Harrison & Sons, 1913. 223 pp. [Obituary notices indexed] (TL 7964) [87]

ROYAL SOCIETY, LONDON. Obituaries of deceased Fellows chiefly for the period 1898–1904 with a general index to previous obituary notices contained in the *Proceedings*, vols. X to LXIV, 1860–1899. London: Harrison & Sons, 1905. 381 pp. (*Proceedings*, vol. 75) (TL7964) [88]

ROYAL SOCIETY, LONDON. Obituary notices of Fellows of the Royal Society. Vol. 1-9. London, 1932–54. [Continued as: *Biographical memoirs* ... 1 (1955)+] (92TL7964) [89]

ROYAL SOCIETY, LONDON. Biographical memoirs of Fellows of the Royal Society, vol. 1+ London, 1955+ (92TL7964) [90]

NATIONAL ACADEMY OF SCIENCES, WASHINGTON. Biographical memoirs of the National Academy of Sciences. Vol. 1+ Washington, 1877. [Vol. 36 (1962) contains an index to vol. 1-35] (92TW446) [91]

RIDOLFI (R.), *Ed.* Biografie e bibliografie degli accademici lincei. Rome: Accademia Nazionale dei Lincei, 1976. 1319 pp. [91A]

Note: Biographical works, not restricted to scientists, are dealt with in Chapter XXIV. All works in the *Handlist* relating to, or containing, biographies (except encyclopedias) have been entered in the subject index under *biographies* or *biographies of scientists.*

Current bibliographies and abstracting journals in the sciences [not listed here, but see p. 31] have sections devoted to biographies, and often contain items not included in the *Isis* Critical Bibliography.

V. SCIENTIFIC MANUSCRIPTS AND ARCHIVES

1. Bibliographies of Catalogues of Manuscripts

JAYAWARDENE (S.A.) Western scientific manuscripts before 1600: a checklist of published catalogues. *Annals of science,* 35 (1978), 143-172. (017/019 and 93JA458) [92]

2. Catalogues of Western Manuscripts
a. Science

MINISTÈRE DE L'INSTRUCTION PUBLIQUE, FRANCE. Catalogue générale des manuscrits des bibliothèques de France. Paris. Par A. Boinet. Tomes I-II. Paris, 1909–14. [Faculté de Médecine, Académie de Médecine, École Supérieure de Pharmacie, Museum d'Histoire Naturelle, École des Mines, École des Ponts et Chausées, École Polytechnique] [93]

SINGER (D.W.) Handlist of Western scientific manuscripts in Great Britain and Ireland dating from before the sixteenth century. British Library, Department of Manuscripts. [Cards in 101 boxes. Details in Skeat (552), pp. 41-43. Microfilm copies at Warburg Institute London, Library of Congress and Cornell University Library] [94]

THORNDIKE (L.) *and* KIBRE (P.) A catalogue of incipits of mediaeval scientific writings in Latin. Rev. ed. London, 1963. 1938 col. (Mediaeval Academy of America publication no. 29) [For supplements *see* 92] (017:091) [95]

CALCOEN (R.) Inventaire des manuscrits scientifiques de la Bibliothèque Royale de Belgique. Brussels: Bibliothèque Royale, 1965–75. 3 vol. (017:091) [97]

GABRIEL (A.L.) A summary catalogue of microfilms of one thousand scientific manuscripts in the Ambrosiana Library, Milan. Notre Dame, Ind.: Medieval Institute, University of Notre Dame, 1968. 439 pp. (017:091) [98]

b. Astrology, Astronomy, Physics

CATALOGUS CODICUM ASTROLOGORUM GRAECORUM. Brussels, 1898–1953. 12 vol. [100]

SAXL (F.) Verzeichnis astrologischer und mythologischer illustrierter Handschriften des lateinischen Mittelalters. *Sitzungsberichte der Heidelberger Akademie der Wissenschaften, philos. hist. Kl.*, 6 (1915), (6-7), 1-143; 16 (1925–26), (2), 1-254. (017:091) [101]

SAXL (F.) Verzeichnis astrologischer und mythologischer illustrierter Handschriften des lateinischen Mittelalters. III. Handschriften in englischen Bibliotheken. Von Fritz Saxl und Hans Meier. IV. Astrological manuscripts in Italian libraries (other than Rome). By Patrick McGurk. London: The Warburg Institute, 1953–66. 3 vol. (017:091) [102]

ZINNER (E.) Verzeichnis der astronomischen Handschriften des deutschen Kulturgebietes. Munich: C.H. Beck, 1925. 544 pp. [Reproduced from handwriting]. (017:091) [103]

LINDBERG (D.C.) A catalogue of medieval and Renaissance optical manuscripts. Toronto: The Pontifical Institute of Mediaeval Studies, 1975. 142 pp. (017:091) [104]

c. Alchemy

UNION ACADÉMIQUE INTERNATIONALE. Catalogue des manuscrits alchimiques grecs. Publiés sous la direction de J. Bidez, F. Cumont, J.L. Heiberg et O. Lagercrantz. Brussels, 1924–36. 8 vols. (017:091) [105]

UNION ACADÉMIQUE INTERNATIONALE. Catalogue of Latin and vernacular alchemical manuscripts in Great Britain and Ireland dating from before the XVIth century. By Dorothea Waley Singer. Brussels: Maurice Laertin, 1928–31. 3 vol. (017:091) [106]

UNION ACADÉMIQUE INTERNATIONALE. Catalogue des manuscrits alchimiques latins. Publié sous la direction de J. Bidez, etc. Brussels, 1939–51. 2 vol. (017:091) [107]

WILSON (W.J.) Catalogue of Latin and vernacular alchemical manuscripts in the United States and Canada. *Osiris,* 6 (1939), 1-836. (017:091) [108]

d. Natural History

REVELLI (P.) I codici Ambrosiani di contenuto geografico. Milan, 1929. 196 pp. (Fontes Ambrosiani, no. 1). [110]

SAWYER (F.C.) A short history of the libraries and list of manuscripts and original drawings in the British Museum (Natural History). *Bulletin, British Museum (Natural History), Hist. ser.,* 4(1971), 77-204. (502TL22168) [112]

BRIDSON (G.D.R.), PHILLIPS (V.C.) *and* HARVEY (A.P.), *Eds.* Natural history manuscript resources in the British Isles. London: Mansell, 1980. 473 pp. [Not a catalogue, but a guide to repositories] (017:091) [113]

e. Medicine

GIACOSA (P.) Magistri salernitani nondum editi. Catalogo ragionato della Esposizione di Storia della Medicina aperta in Torino nel 1898. Turin: Fratelli Bocca, 1901. 723 pp. [114]

DIELS (H.) Die Handschriften der antiken Ärzte. Berlin, 1905–1908. 3 pts. 345 pp. [Originally published in *Abhandlungen der K. Preussischen Akademie der Wissenschaften, philos. hist. Kl.* 1905, 1906, 1907] [115]

PANSIER (P.) Catalogue des manuscrits médicaux des bibliothèques de France. *Archiv für Geschichte der Medizin,* 2 (1908), 1-46, 385-403. (93JA 7515) [116]

WELLCOME HISTORICAL MEDICAL LIBRARY, LONDON (*now* Wellcome Institute for the History of Medicine]. Catalogue of Western manuscripts on medicine and science in the Library. By S.A.J. Moorat. London, 1962–76. 3 vol. (017:091) [117]

MACKINNEY (L.C.) Medical illustrations in mediaeval manuscripts. London: Wellcome Historical Medical Library, 1965. 263 pp. [Pp. 103-185: Medical miniatures in extant manuscripts. A check list compiled with the assistance of Thomas Herndon] (61:93) [118]

SINGER (D.W.) *and* ANDERSON (A.) Catalogue of Latin and vernacular plague texts in Great Britain and Eire in manuscripts written before the sixteenth century. Paris, 1950. 274 pp. (Collection de Travaux de l'Académie Internationale d'Histoire des Sciences, 5) [typescript] [119]

BECCARIA (A.) I codici di medicina del periodo presalernitano, secoli IX, X, XI. Rome: Edizioni di Storia e Letteratura, 1956. 500 pp. (017:091) [120]

BAZZI (F.) Catalogo dei manoscritti e degli incunaboli di interesse medico-naturalistico dell'Ambrosiana e della Braidense. Bergamo, 1961. 189 pp. (Quaderni di "Castalia", n.7) (017:091) [122]

WICKERSHEIMER (E.) Les manuscrits latins de médecine du haut moyen âge dans les bibliothèques de France. Paris: Éditions du CNRS, 1966. 254 pp. (Documents, études et répertoires publiés par l'Institut de Recherche et d'Histoire des Textes, 11) (017:091) [123]

NATIONAL LIBRARY OF MEDICINE. A summary checklist of medical manuscripts on microfilm held by the National Library of Medicine. Bethesda, Md., 1968. xiv pp. (017:091) [124]

3. *Catalogues of Oriental Manuscripts*

STEINSCHNEIDER (M.) Die arabischen Übersetzungen aus dem Griechischen. Graz: Akademische Druck- u. Verlagsanstalt, 1960. 381 pp. [Originally published in 1889, 1891, 1893, 1896 as a series of articles] (5"04/16": 93) [126]

STEINSCHNEIDER (M.) Die hebraeischen Uebersetzungen des Mittelalters und die Juden als Dolmetscher. Graz: Akademische Druck- u. Verlagsanstalt, 1956. 1077 pp. [Reprint of the 1893 Berlin edition] (5"04/16":93) [127]

SUTER (H.) Die Mathematiker und Astronomen der Araber und ihre Werke. *Abhandlungen zur Geschichte der mathematischen Wissenschaften,* 10 (1900), 1-278; 14 (1902), 157-185. [See also *Isis*, 18 (1932), 166-183] (93JZ438A) [128]

PINGREE (D.) Census of the exact sciences in Sanskrit. *Memoirs of the American Philosophical Society,* 81 (1970), 1-60; 86 (1971), 1-147; 111 (1976), 1-208. ["Preliminary exploration and organization of the vast mass of Sanskrit and Sanskrit-influenced literature devoted to the exact sciences." Both a bibliography of published literature and a survey of MSS. Includes a bio-bibliography of some 1,500 scientists] (5(5):93) [129]

UNION ACADÉMIQUE INTERNATIONALE. Katalog der arabischen alchimistischen Handschriften Deutschlands ... in Auftrage der Deutsche Akademie der Wissenschaften zu Berlin. Bearbeitet von Alfred Siggel. Berlin, 1945–1956. 3 vols. (017:091) [131]

WELLCOME HISTORICAL MEDICAL LIBRARY, LONDON (*now* Wellcome Institute for the History of Medicine). A catalogue of Arabic manuscripts on medicine and science in the Library. By A.Z. Iskandar. London, 1967. 256 pp. (017:091) [132]

4. *Archives of Scientists and Scientific Institutions*

BLUHM (R.K.) A guide to the archives of the Royal Society and to other manuscripts in its possession. *Notes and records of the Royal Society of London,* 12 (1956), 21-39. (5TL 79645) [133]

ACADEMY OF NATURAL SCIENCES, PHILADELPHIA. Guide to the manuscript collections in the Academy ... Compiled by Venia T. Phillips and Maurice E. Phillips. Philadelphia, 1963. 553 pp. (017:091) [134]

SMITHSONIAN INSTITUTION, WASHINGTON. Archives and special collections of the Smithsonian Institution, no. 1+ Washington, 1971+ (930.253) [135]

KUHN (T.S.), HEILBRON, (J.L.), FORMAN (P.) *and* ALLEN (L.) Sources for history of quantum physics. An inventory and report. Philadelphia: American Philosophical Society, 1967. 176 pp. (*Memoirs*, vol 68). Suppl. 1973. 7 pp. (016:93:530.1) [136]

AMERICAN INSTITUTE OF PHYSICS. *Center for History and Philosophy of Physics.* National catalog of sources for history of physics, report no. 1+ New York, 1969+ (930.25TU2362) [137]

WARNOW (J.N.) A selection of manuscript collections at American repositories. New York: American Institute of Physics, 1969. 73 pp. (National Catalog of Sources for the History of Physics, report no. 1) (930.25TU2362) [138]

MACLEOD (R.M.) *and* FRIDAY (J.R.) Archives of British men of science. London: Mansell, 1972. microfiche. [Mainly scientists who flourished between 1870 and 1950] (017:091) [139]

CONTEMPORARY SCIENTIFIC ARCHIVES CENTRE, OXFORD. Progress report no. 1+ 1973+ [The Centre's work is described by Margaret Gowing in *Notes and records of the Royal Society,* 34 (1979), 123-131] (930.25TO747) [140]

HOUNSHELL (D.A.) Manuscripts in US depositories relating to the history of electrical science and technology. Washington: National Museum of History and Technology, 1973. 116 pp. (930.253) [141]

SURVEY OF SOURCES FOR THE HISTORY OF BIOCHEMISTRY AND MOLECULAR BIOLOGY, PHILADELPHIA. Survey of sources newsletter, vol. 1, no. 1+ 1975+ (930.25TU5745) [142]

BEARMAN (David) *and* EDSALL (John T.), *Eds.* Archival sources for the history of biochemistry and molecular biology: a reference guide and report. Boston: American Academy of Arts and Sciences; Philadelphia: American Philosophical Society, 1980. 338 pp.; 6-fiche suppl. [142A]

HISTORICAL MANUSCRIPTS COMMISSION, GREAT BRITAIN. Manuscript papers of British scientists, 1600–1940. [*In press.* Typescript available for consultation at the National Register of Archives] [146]

MERZBACH (Uta) Guide to mathematical papers in United States repositories. Wilmington, Del.: Scholarly Resources [*In press*] [146A]

VI. SCIENTIFIC LITERATURE

1. *Bibliographical Guides*
   a. *General*
   b. *Mathematics and Physics*
   c. *Natural History*
   d. *Medicine*
2. *Guides to Abstracts and Abstracting Services*
3. *Bibliographies*
   a. *Science*
   b. *Mathematics*
   c. *Astronomy*
   d. *Chemistry*
   e. *Natural History*
   f. *Medicine*
   g. *Philosophy*

1. *Bibliographical Guides*

a. *General*

MALCLÈS (L.N.) Les sources du travail bibliographique. Tome 3. Bibliographies spécialisées (sciences exactes et techniques). Geneva: Librairie Droz, 1958. 575 pp. [*See* 680] (011/016) [147]

WALFORD (A.J.) Guide to reference material. 4th ed. Vol. 1. Science and technology. London: Library Assn., 1980. 697 pp. [*See* 682] (011/016) [148]

JENKINS (F.B.) Science reference sources. 5th ed. Cambridge: MIT Pr., 1969. 231 pp. (011/016) [149]

GROGAN (D.) Science and technology: an introduction to the literature. 3rd ed. London: Clive Bingley, 1976. 343 pp. (016:5) [150]

b. Mathematics and Physics

PARKE (N.G.) Guide to the literature of mathematics and physics. 2nd ed. New York: Dover, 1958. 436 pp. (016:5) [151]

c. Natural History

BRIDSON (G.) *and* HARVEY (A.P.) A checklist of natural history bibliographies and bibliographical scholarship. *Journal of the Society for the Bibliography of Natural History*, 5 (1971), 428-467; 6 (1973), 263-292. (93TL8333) [152]

d. Medicine

BLAKE (John B.) *and* ROOS (C.), *Eds.* Medical reference works 1679–1966: a selected bibliography. Chicago: Medical Library Assn., 1967. 343 pp. [Classified, annotated bibliography of 2703 reference books. 1-413: medicine (general); 414-832: history of medicine; 833-2703: special subjects; 1481-1537: medical libraries; 2668-2676: authorship. 1st suppl. (46 pp.), 1970] (016:61) [153]

ARCHIMBAUD (J.) Bibliographie et recherche documentaire en médecine et pharmacie. Rueil-Malmaison: Sandoz, 1970–72. 2 vol. [Review: *Revue d'histoire de pharmacie*, 60 (1972), 291-293; 61 (1973), 444-445] [154]

2. Guides to Abstracts and Abstracting Services

[Abstracting and indexing journals in science are not given in this *Handlist*. In addition to the guides 155-158 there is an article by C.F. Mayer in Sarton's *Horus* (3), pp. 105-110. Some abstracting journals contain sections devoted to the history (and biography) of their subject: e.g., *Astronomischer Jahresbericht; Jahrbuch über die Fortschritte der*

Mathematik; Chemical abstracts; Zoological record. See also notes to the 81st *Isis* Critical Bibliography in *Isis*, 47 (1956), 248-251]

LIBRARY OF CONGRESS. A guide to the world's abstracting and indexing services in science and technology. Washington, 1963. 183 pp. (NFSAIS report no. 102) [155]

NATIONAL LENDING LIBRARY FOR SCIENCE AND TECHNOLOGY (*now* British Library, Lending Division). KWIC index to the English language abstracting and indexing publications currently being received by the Library. Boston Spa, 1967. 46 pp. (016:016) [156]

NATIONAL REFERENCE LIBRARY OF SCIENCE AND INVENTION (*now* Science Reference Library). Abstracting and bibliographical periodicals held by NRLSI. Ed. by A. Mukherjee; London, 1972. 55 pp. (05) [157]

OWEN (D.B.) *and* HANCHEY (M.) Abstracts and indexes in science and technology. A descriptive guide. Metuchen, N.J.: Scarecrow Press, 1974. 154 pp. (011/016) [158]

[*See also* 824, 825 and 899]

3. Bibliographies
a. Science

KLEBS (A.C.) Incunabula scientifica et medica. Short title list. *Osiris*, 4 (1938), 40-238. (93J092 and 017:091) [159]

STILLWELL (M.B.) The awakening interest in science during the first century of printing, 1450–1550. An annotated list of first editions. New York: Bibliographical Society of America, 1970. 399 pp. (017:093) [160]

THORNTON (J.L.) *and* TULLY (R.I.J.) Scientific books, libraries and collectors: a study of bibliography and the book trade in relation to science. 3rd rev. ed. London: Library Assn., 1971. 508 pp. Suppl. (covering the years 1969–1975). 1978. 192 pp. (5(02):93) [161-162]

b. Mathematics

RICCARDI (P.) Biblioteca matematica italiana dalle origini della stampa ai primi anni del secolo XIX. Modena, 1873–1928. 7 pt. [Facsimile reproduction 1952 by Görlich, Milan. Annotated bibliography of some 8,000 works on mathematics, physics and astronomy. Detailed subject index] (016:51) [163]

BIERENS DE HAAN (D.) Bibliographie néerlandaise historique-scientifique des ouvrages importants dont les auteurs sont nés aux 16e, 17e, et 18e siècles, sur les sciences mathématiques et physiques. Nieuwkoop: de Graaf, 1960. [Reprint of the 1883 edition. Subject index] (017:093) [163A]

c. Astronomy

HOUZEAU (J.) *and* LANCASTER (A.) Bibliographie générale de l'astronomie jusqu'en 1880. General bibliography of astronomy to the year 1880. Nouvelle éd. London: Holland Press, 1964. 2 vol. in 3 pt. [First published 1882–89. Subjects include: astrology; history; biographies and correspondence. Vol. 1, pp. 1631-33 contain a guide to the MSS listed. Vol. 2 is devoted to periodical literature] (016:52) [164]

INTERNATIONAL ASTRONOMICAL UNION. Bibliography of astronomy 1881–1898. Prepared by P. Stroobant, 1932–1936, and by the Belgian National Committee for Astronomy, 1938–1965. [Microfilm]. [Fills the gap between (164) and *Astronomischer Jahresbericht*, 1 (1899)] (016:52) [165]

d. Chemistry

BOLTON (H.C.) Select bibliography of chemistry, 1492–1902. Washington: Smithsonian Institution, 1893–1904. 4 vol. (016:54) [166]

PRITCHARD (Alan) Alchemy: a bibliography of English-language writings. London: Routledge & Kegan Paul; Library Assn., 1980. 439 pp. (016:133.5:54) [166A]

e. Natural History

HALLER (Albrecht von) Bibliotheca botanica. Zurich, 1771–72. 2 vol. [167]

DRYANDER (J.) Catalogus bibliothecae historico-naturalis Josephi Banks. London, 1796–1800. 5 vol. [Classified subject catalogue of books, journal articles and theses in zoology, botany and mineralogy. Reprinted by Johnson Reprint Corporation 1966] (O.B. DRY) [167A]

PRITZEL (G.A.) Thesaurus literaturae botanicae omnium gentium, inde a rerum botanicarum initiis ad nostra usque tempora. 2nd ed. Leipzig: Brockhaus, 1872. 576 pp. (016:58) [168]

KNIGHT (D.M.) Natural science books in English, 1600–1900. London: Batsford, 1972. 262 pp. (5(02):93) [169]

HENREY (B.) British botanical and horticultural literature before 1800: comprising a history and bibliography of botanical and horticultural books printed in England, Scotland and Ireland. London: Oxford Univ. Pr., 1975. 3 vol. (016:58) [170]

SIMON (Hans Reiner) Die Bibliographie der Biologie: eine analytische Darstellung. Stuttgart: Hiersemann, 1977.

315 pp. (Bibliothek des Buchwesens, Bd. 4) (016:57) [171]

f. Medicine

HALLER (Albrecht von) Bibliotheca chirugica. Berne, 1774–75. 2 vol. [172]

HALLER (Albrecht von) Bibliotheca anatomica. Zurich, 1774–77. 2 vol. (O.B. HAL) [173]

PAULY (A.) Bibliographie des sciences médicales. Bibliographie, biographie, histoire, épidémies, topographies, endémies. Paris: Tross, 1874. 1758 pp. [Reprinted London 1954] (016:93:61) [174]

HALLER (Albrecht von) Bibliothecae medicinae practicae . . . tomus I - IV. Berne, 1776–88. 4 vol. [175]

THORNTON (John L.) Medical books, libraries and collectors: a study of bibliography and the book trade in relation to the medical sciences. 2nd rev. ed. London: Andre Deutsch, 1966. 445 pp. [First published 1949] [176]

GARRISON (F.H.) A medical bibliography (Garrison and Morton). An annotated check-list of texts illustrating the history of medicine. By Leslie T. Morton. 3rd ed. London: Andre Deutsch, 1970. 872 pp. (016:93:61) [177]

LEITNER (H.) Bibliography to the ancient medical authors. (The Historical Medical Institute of the University of Vienna). Berne: Hans Huber Publishers, 1973. 61 pp. (016:93:61) [178]

g. Philosophy

VARET (G.) Manuel de bibliographie philosophique. Paris: Presses Univ. de France, 1956. 2 vol. (SML) [179]

ROBERT (Jean Dominique) Philosophie et science. Éléments de bibliographie. Paris: Beauchesne, 1968. 384 pp. (016:113/119) [180]

GEORGE (Richard T. de) A guide to philosophical bibliography and research. New York: Meredith Corporation, 1971. 141 pp. [181]

MITCHAM (C.) *and* MACKEY (Robert) Bibliography of the philosophy of technology. Chicago: Univ. of Chicago Pr., 1973. 205 pp. [First published in *Technology and culture*, vol. 14] (93JT3825) [182]

TOBEY (J.L.) The history of ideas: a bibliographical introduction. Santa Barbara, Calif.: Clio Books, 1975–77. 2 vol. [Vol. 1: Classical antiquity; Vol. 2: Medieval and early modern Europe] (016:93:001) [183]

GUERRY (Herbert) A bibliography of philosophical bibliographies. Westport, Conn.: Greenwood Pr., 1977. 332 pp. [184]

VII. CATALOGUES OF SCIENTIFIC BOOKS

1. General

BONCOMPAGNI (B.) Catalogo della insigne biblioteca appartenuta alla chiara memoria del Principe D. Baldassarre Boncompagni. Parte prima. Matematica, scienze naturali ecc. Rome, 1895. 511 pp. (017:5) [185]

KAISERLICHES PATENTAMT, GERMANY. Katalog der Bibliothek des Kaiserlichen Patentamts. Stand von 1. Oktober 1923. Berlin, 1923. 3 vol. [The library is now in Munich] [186]

JOHN CRERAR LIBRARY, CHICAGO. Author-title catalog. Boston: G.K. Hall, 1967. 35 vol. (017:5) [187]

JOHN CRERAR LIBRARY, CHICAGO. Classified subject catalog. Boston: G.K. Hall, 1967. 42 vol. (017:5) [188]

AMERICAN PHILOSOPHICAL SOCIETY. *Library*. Catalog of books in the library. Westport, Conn.: Greenwood, 1970. 28 vol. [189]

ROLLER (D.H.D.) *and* GOODMAN (M.M.) The catalogue of the history of science collections of the University of Oklahoma libraries. London: Mansell, 1976. 2 vol. (017:93:5) [190]

DEUTSCHES MUSEUM. *Bibliothek.* Katalog der Druckschriften bis 1750. Libri rari. Bearbeitet von Elske Neidhardt und Margret Nida-Rümelin. Munich: Ziffer, 1976. 312 pp. (017:093) [191]

UNION CATALOGUE OF SCIENTIFIC LIBRARIES IN THE UNIVERSITY OF CAMBRIDGE. Books published before 1801. Compiled at the Scientific Periodicals Library, University of Cambridge. London: Mansell, 1977. [Microfiche] [191A]

DEUTSCHES MUSEUM. *Bibliothek.* Kataloge der Bibliothek des Deutschen Museums. Autorenkatalog. Literatur bis Erscheinungsjahr 1976. Munich: Verlag Dokumentation, 1978. [*In progress*] (017:5) [192]

BIBLIOTHÈQUE SAINTE-GENEVIÈVE, PARIS. Catalogue des ouvrages imprimés au XVIe siècle. Sciences–Techniques–Médecine. Redigé par Jacqueline Linet et Denise Hillard. Paris: K.G. Saur, 1980. 493 pp. [192A]

2. *Mathematics and Astronomy*

LIBRI (G.) Catalogue of the mathematical, historical, bibliographical and miscellaneous portions of the celebrated library of M. Guglielmo Libri. London: Sotheby, 1861. 4 vol. [193]

GROENFELDT (S.) Systematisk foesteckning oefver G. Mittag-Lefflers matematiska bibliotek. Uppsala, 1915. 352 pp. [See *Isis*, 62 (1971), 363-374] (Warburg Institute) [193A]

ROYAL OBSERVATORY, EDINBURGH. *Crawford Library*. Catalogue of the Crawford Library. Edinburgh, 1890. 497 pp. Supplement. [A computer-produced index to the whole collection] 1977. 112 pp. [*See* 919A] (017:52) [194]

GRASSI (G.) Union catalogue of printed books of the XV and XVI centuries in astronomical European observatories. Rome: Astronomical Observatory, 1977. 105 pp. (017:52) [195]

SAUVENIER-GOFFIN (E.) Les sciences mathématiques et physiques à travers le fonds ancien de la Bibliothèque de l'Université de Liège. Liège, 1961. 427 pp. (*Mémoires, Société Royale des Sciences de Liège*, (4), 19 (1957), (2); (5), 5 (1961)) [196]

3. Alchemy and Chemistry

FERGUSON (John) Bibliotheca chemica: a catalogue of the alchemical, chemical and pharmaceutical books in the collection of the late James Young of Kelly and Durris. Glasgow: Maclehose, 1906. 2 vol. [Classic work of reference. Some 1,400 titles, extensively annotated. Collection bequeathed to Anderson's College, Glasgow, *now* University of Strathclyde] (017:54:133.5) [196A]

UNIVERSITY OF GLASGOW. *Library*. Catalogue of the Ferguson collection of books, mainly relating to alchemy, chemistry, witchcraft and gipsies. Glasgow: Maclehose, 1943-55. 2 vol. & suppl. [Part of Ferguson's working library. "Superior in scope, variety and rarity of constitutional elements to the Young collection" (196A). Not annotated] (017:54:133.5) [197]

DUVEEN (D.I.) Bibliotheca alchemica et chemica. An annotated catalogue of printed books on alchemy, chemistry and cognate subjects. London: Weil, 1949. 669 pp. [Some 3,000 titles. See *J. chem. educ.*, 29 (1952), 244-247. Part of the collection has been acquired by the University of Wisconsin libraries] (017:54) [198]

4. Natural History

RADCLIFFE LIBRARY, OXFORD. Catalogue of books on natural science. Oxford, 1877. 566 pp. (017:57) [199]

BRITISH MUSEUM (NATURAL HISTORY). *Library.* Catalogue of the books, manuscripts, maps and drawings. London, 1903-40. 8 vol. (017:5) [200]

ROTHAMSTED EXPERIMENTAL STATION. *Library.* Catalogue of printed books and pamphlets on agriculture published between 1471 and 1840. 2nd ed. Compiled by Mary S. Aslin. Harpenden, 1940. 293 pp. (016:63) [201]

HUNT BOTANICAL LIBRARY. Catalogue of botanical books in the collection of Rachel McMasters Miller Hunt. Compiled by Jane Quinby and Allan Stevenson. Pittsburgh, Pa., 1958–61. 2 vol. in 3. (017:58) [202]

SOUTHAMPTON UNIVERSITY LIBRARY. Catalogue of the Walter Frank Perkins Agricultural Library. Southampton, 1961. 291 pp. (017:63) [203]

GOURRY (H.P.) Répertoire bibliographique de la Bibliothèque Arpad Plesch. Mille et un livres botaniques. (Catalogue raisonné des livres curieux et notables de la Bibliothèque Botanique Arpad Plesch). Brussels: Arcade, 1973. 517 pp. (017:58) [204]

5. Medicine

ROYAL MEDICAL AND CHIRURGICAL SOCIETY OF LONDON. Catalogue of the library of the Royal Medical and Chirurgical Society. Compiled by B.R. Wheatley. London, 1879. 3 vol. [205]

U.S. SURGEON GENERAL'S OFFICE. *Library* (*now* National Library of Medicine). Index catalogue of the library of the Surgeon General's Office, United States Army: authors and subjects. Washington: Govt. Printing Office, 1880–1961. 61 vol. [A dictionary catalogue, serving both as a bibliography and a library catalogue. For a detailed description, *see* Winchell/Sheehy (687)] (016:61) [206]

SALLANDER (H.) Bibliotheca Walleriana. The books illustrating the history of medicine and science, collected by Dr. Erik Waller. Stockholm: Almquist and Wiksell, 1955. 2 vol. (017:93:5) [207]

WILLIAM DAWSON AND SONS, LONDON. Medicine and science: a bibliographical catalogue of historical and rare books from the 15th to the 20th century. (Catalogue no. 91). London, 1956. 610 pp. [pp. 597-610: subject index] (017:61) [208]

NATIONAL LIBRARY OF MEDICINE, U.S. A catalogue of sixteenth century printed books. Compiled by Richard J. Durling. Bethesda, Md., 1967. 698 pp. (017:61) [209]

OSLER (Sir William) Bibliotheca Osleriana. A catalogue of books illustrating the history of medicine and science . . . bequeathed to McGill University. 2nd ed. Montreal: McGill-Queen's Univ. Pr., 1969. 792 pp. (017:61) [210]

UNIVERSITY OF READING. *Library*. The Cole Library of early medicine and zoology: catalogue of books and pamphlets (monographs and principal papers). By Nellie B. Eales. Reading, 1969–75. 2 vol. (017:61) [211]

NEW YORK ACADEMY OF MEDICINE. *Library*. Author and subject catalogs of the library. Boston: G.K. Hall, 1970. 43 vol. (author catalog), 34 vol. (subject catalog) [212]

UNIVERSITY OF MANCHESTER. *Library*. Catalogue of medical books, 1480–1700. Compiled by E. Parkinson. Manchester: Univ. Pr., 1972. 399 pp. (017:61) [213]

WELLCOME HISTORICAL MEDICAL LIBRARY (*now* Wellcome Institute for the History of Medicine). Catalogue of printed books. London, 1962–76; 3 vol. [Vol. 1: Books printed before 1641; vol. 2, 3: Books printed from 1641 to 1850 (A–L). *In progress*] (017:61) [213A]

HERZOG AUGUST BIBLIOTHEK, WOLFENBÜTTEL. Verzeichnis medizinischer und naturwissenschaftlicher Drucke, 1472–1830. Bearbeitet von Ursula Zachert. Nendeln, Liechtenstein: Kraus-Thomson, 1976+ [*In progress*] (017:5) [214]

WELLCOME INSTITUTE FOR THE HISTORY OF MEDICINE. Subject catalogue of the history of medicine and related sciences. Nendeln, Liechtenstein: KTO Press, 1979+. [To be completed in 3 sections, 16 vol.: subject, biographical, topographical] (017:61:93) [215]

NATIONAL LIBRARY OF MEDICINE, U.S. A short title catalogue of eighteenth century printed books. Compiled by John B. Blake. Bethesda, Md., 1979. 501 pp. [215A]

6. *Engineering*

SOCIETY OF TELEGRAPH ENGINEERS (*now* Institution of Electrical Engineers). Catalogue of books and papers relating to electricity, magnetism, the electric telegraph, etc. including the Ronalds Library. London: Spon, 1880. 564 pp. (016:537) [216]

ENGINEERING SOCIETIES LIBRARY, NEW YORK. Classed subject catalog. Boston: G.K. Hall, 1963. 13 vol. suppl. (017:62) [217]

AMERICAN INSTITUTE OF ELECTRICAL ENGINEERS. *Library*. Catalogue of the Wheeler gift of books, pamphlets and periodicals. Edited by William D. Weaver. With introduction, descriptive and critical notes by Brother Potamian. New York, 1909. 2 vol. (017:537) [218]

7. *Maritime Affairs, Exploration*

ROYAL GEOGRAPHICAL SOCIETY, LONDON. Catalogue of the library. [3rd ed.] Compiled by Hugh Robert Mill. London: John Murray, 1895. 833 pp. [Appendices: collections of voyages and travels (pp. 525-612); Government, anonymous and other miscellaneous publns. (pp. 615-769); Transactions and periodicals (pp. 771-833)] (017:91) [218A]

MARINER'S MUSEUM, NEWPORT NEWS, Va. Dictionary catalog of the library. Boston, Mass.: G.K. Hall & Co., 1964. 9 vol. [44,000 vol. pertaining to shipbuilding, navigation, voyages and exploration, naval history, merchant shipping and other maritime subjects. Includes a separate catalogue of books published from 1497 to 1825 arranged chronologically. Vol. 9, pp. 789 ff. contain a bibliography of fleetlists, shipowners and shipyards] (017.1:629.12) [218B]

MINISTRY OF DEFENCE, LONDON. *Naval Library*. Author and subject catalogue. Boston, Mass.: G.K. Hall & Co., 1967. 5 vol. (017:359) [218C]

NATIONAL MARITIME MUSEUM, GREENWICH. Catalogue of the library. London: HMSO, 1968–76. 5 vol. [Voyages and travel; biography; atlases and cartography; naval history. *In progress*] (017:910) [218D]

VIII. SCIENTIFIC PERIODICALS

1. *Bibliographical Guides*
2. *Bibliographies*
3. *Union Catalogues*
4. *Library Catalogues*
5. *Indexes of Periodical Literature*

1. *Bibliographical Guides*

FOWLER (M.J.) Guides to scientific periodicals: annotated bibliography. London: Library Assn., 1966. 318 pp. (05) [219]

2. *Bibliographies*

SCUDDER (S.H.) Catalogue of scientific serials of all countries including the transactions of learned societies in the natural, physical and mathematical sciences 1633–1876. Cambridge, Mass.: Harvard Univ. Pr., 1879. 358 pp. (05:011) [220]

BOLTON (H.C.) Catalogue of scientific and technical periodicals, 1665–1895; together with chronological tables and a library check-list. 2nd ed. Washington: Smithsonian Instn., 1897. 1247 pp. (05:011) [221]

GARRISON (F.H.) The medical and scientific periodicals of the 17th and 18th centuries. With a revised catalogue and check-list. *Bulletin of the Institute of the History of Medicine*. 2 (1934), 285-343: 32 (1958), 456-474. (5(02):93) [222]

SARTON (G.) *and* MAYER (C.F.) Journals and serials concerning the history (and philosophy) of science. In: G. Sarton, *Horus: a guide to the history of science* (Waltham, Mass.: Chronica Botanica, 1952), pp. 194-248. (016:93:5 and 5:93) [222A]

3. *Union Catalogues*

UNIVERSITY OF LONDON. *Library*. Union list of periodicals on mathematics and allied subjects in London libraries. 2nd ed. London, 1968. 139 pp. (05:017.11) [223]

WORLD LIST OF SCIENTIFIC PERIODICALS PUBLISHED IN THE YEARS 1900–1960. 4th ed. London: Butterworth, 1963–65. 3 vol. [Some 60,000 titles; separate list of international conferences in each vol. Holdings of about 300 British libraries. Contd. in 852. For titles no longer held by the Science Museum Library *see* 227] (SML) [224] *

BULTINGAIRE (L.) Inventaire des périodiques scientifiques des bibliothèques de Paris. Paris: Masson, 1924–39. Suppléments I–II. 3 vol. (05:017:11) [225]

BODLEIAN LIBRARY. Union list of serials in the science area, Oxford. Stage 2 (incorporating stage 1). Oxford, 1970. (05:017:11) [226]

4. *Library Catalogues*

SCIENCE MUSEUM LIBRARY. Handlist of short titles of current periodicals in the Science Library transferred from the Science Library to the NLLST in 1961 and 1962. An edition prepared by photocopying the visible index. London, 1962. 382 pp. [NLLST = British Library, Lending Division] (SML only) [227]

SCIENCE MUSEUM LIBRARY. Current periodicals in the Science Museum Library. A hand list. 9th ed. London, 1965. 196 pp. [Still useful. Gives details of holdings and changes of title] (SML) [228]

SCIENCE MUSEUM LIBRARY. Periodicals on open access. Lists A, B, C, D. London, Nov. 1977. [Latest edition is on microfiche] (SML) [229]

BRITISH MUSEUM (NATURAL HISTORY) LIBRARY. List of serial publications in the British Museum (Natural History) Library. 2nd ed. London, 1975. 3 vol. (05:017) [230]

NATIONAL REFERENCE LIBRARY OF SCIENCE AND INVENTION (*now* Science Reference Library). Periodical publications in the . . . Library. London, 1969–70. 3 vol. [On microfiche since 1974] (SML) [231]

HUNT BOTANICAL LIBRARY. B-P-H. Botanico-periodicum-huntianum. Pittsburgh, 1968. 1063 pp. [Gives locations of entries in *Union list of serials*, 3rd ed. (854)] (Botany Library, Nat. Hist. Museum) [232]

CENTRE NATIONAL DE RECHERCHE SCIENTIFIQUE. *Bibliothèque du Centre de Documentation Scientifique et Technique*. Catalogue des périodiques reçus, ... classé par ordre alphabétique de titres. 3e éd. Paris, 1977. 2 vol. (016:5) [232A]

CENTRE NATIONAL DE RECHERCHE SCIENTIFIQUE. *Bibliothèque du Centre de Documentation Scientifique et Technique*. Index permuté des périodiques reçus. 3e éd. Paris, 1977. 2 vol. (016:5) [232B]

5. *Indexes of Periodical Literature*

[*See also* 155–158]

GEUS (Armin), *Ed.* Indices naturwissenschaftlich-medizinischer Periodica bis 1850. Band 1: Der Naturforscher 1774–1804. Band 2. Teil 1. Die chemischen Zeitschriften des Lorenz von Crell. Bearbeitet von Dietrich von Engelhardt. Stuttgart: Hiersemann, 1971–74. 2 vol. (016:5) [233]

REUSS (J.D.) Repertorium commentationum a societatibus litterariis editarum. Göttingen: Dieterich, 1801–1821. 16 vol. [Index to publications of learned societies up to 1800. Reprinted 1962 Burt Franklin, New York] (016:5) [234]

ROYAL SOCIETY OF LONDON. Catalogue of scientific papers, 1800–1900. London and Cambridge, 1867–1925. 19 vol. Subject index in 4 vols. (pure maths., mechanics, physics *only*). [Intended to contain every scientific memoir which appeared in the various Transactions and Proceedings of scientific societies and in scientific journals. Includes (from 2nd ser.) inaugural addresses, biographies, and history of science. Index volumes contain sections for history and biography] (016:5) [235]

INTERNATIONAL CATALOGUE OF SCIENTIFIC LITERATURE, 1901–1914. Published for the International Council by the Royal Society. London, 1902–21. 14 vol. in 254. [Each annual issue divided into 17 sections (A–R). An outgrowth of the Royal Society's *Catalogue* (235), intended to cover the literature after 1900. Abandoned during World War I] (016:5) [236]

PROCKTER (C.E.), *Comp.* 'The Engineer' index, 1856–1959. Names and subjects. London: Morgan Bros., 1964. 216 pp. [Index to *The Engineer.* Includes obituaries] (016:62/69) [237]

IX. PATENTS AND INVENTIONS

SEVERANCE (B.) Manual of foreign patents. Washington: Patent Office Society, 1935. 161 pp. [238]

NEWBY (F.) How to find out about patents. Oxford: Pergamon, 1967. 177 pp. (016:62/69) [239]

HOUGHTON (B.) Technical information sources: a guide to patents, standards and technical reports literature. London: Bingley, 1967. 107 pp. [240]

SCIENCE REFERENCE LIBRARY, LONDON. Literature in the British patents section. London, 1976. 8 pp. (Aids to readers, No. 10) (025.5REF) [241]

WOODCROFT (B.) Alphabetical index of patentees of inventions. With an introduction and appendix of additions and corrections compiled in the Patent Office Library. London: Evelyn, Adams and Mackay, 1969. 647 pp. [First published 1854] (SML) [242]

PATENT OFFICE, LONDON. Titles of patents of invention, chronologically arranged from March 2, 1617 to October 1, 1852. By Bennet Woodcroft. London, 1854. 2 vol. [Covers patents 1–14359] (SML) [243]

PATENT OFFICE, LONDON. Subject-matter index of patents of invention from March 2, 1617 to October 1, 1852. By Bennet Woodcroft. 2nd ed. London, 1857. 2 vol. (SML) [244]

BAKER (Ronald) New and improved. Inventors and inventions that have changed the modern world. London: British Library, 1976. 168 pp. (608:93) [245]

RIMMER (B.M.) Guide to German patent and trade mark publications (including East Germany). London: Science Reference Library, 1979. 24 pp. (016:608.3 (430)) [245A]

UNITED STATES PATENT OFFICE. Subject-matter index of patents for inventions issued by the United States Patent Office from 1790 to 1873 inclusive. Compiled by M.D. Leggett. Washington, 1874. 3 vol. [Reprinted by Arno Press, New York, 1976] [246]

RIMMER (B.M.) Guide to United States patent and trade mark literature. London: Science Reference Library, 1980. 24 pp. [*See also* N. Reingold, "U.S. Patent Office records as sources for the history of invention and technological property," *Technology and culture*, 1 (1960), 156-167] [247]

FELDHAUS (F.M.) Lexikon der Erfindungen und Entdeckungen auf den Gebieten der Naturwissenschaften und Technik in chronologischer Übersicht mit Personen- und Sachregister. Heidelberg: Carl Winter, 1904. 144 pp. (5:93) [248]

FELDHAUS (F.M.) *and* KLINCKOWSTROEM (*Graf* Carl von) Bibliographie der erfindungsgeschichtlichen Literatur. *Geschichtsblätter für Technik und Industrie*, 10 (1923), 1-21. (93JG56) [249]

ALPHANDÉRY (M.F.) Dictionnaire des inventeurs français. Paris: Collection Seghers, 1962. 371 pp. (92:62) [250]

MINISTÈRE DE L'INDUSTRIE ET DU COMMERCE. Brevets d'invention français 1791–1902. Un siècle de progrès technique. Paris, 1958. 321 pp. (608.3:93) [251]

X. MUSEUMS

1. *Bibliographies*
2. *Directories*
   a. *International*
   b. *Great Britain*
   c. *France*
   d. *Germany*
   e. *United States and Canada*

1. *Bibliographies*

MURRAY (David) Museums, their history and their use, with a bibliography and a list of museums in the U.K. Glasgow: Maclehose, 1904. 3 vol. [252]

SMITH (Ralph C.) Bibliography of museums and museum work. Washington: American Assn. of Museums, 1928. 302 pp. [253]

CLAPP (J.) Museum publications: a classified list and index of books. New York: Scarecrow, 1962. 2 vol. (013:069) [254]

BIBLIOGRAPHY OF MUSEUM AND ART GALLERY PUBLICATIONS AND AUDIO-VISUAL AIDS IN GREAT BRITAIN AND IRELAND. Cambridge: Chadwyck-Healey 1980. 450 pp. [Many items listed here are not found in *Books in print* or in any other bibliography] (013:069) [255]

2. *Directories*
a. *International*

HUDSON (Kenneth) *and* NICHOLS (Ann) The directory of museums. London: Macmillan, 1975. 864 pp. [Pp. 603-859: Classified index] (069 REF) [256]

MUSEUMS OF THE WORLD: a directory of 17,500 museums in 150 countries, including a subject index. 2nd ed. Pullach (Munich): Verlag Dokumentation, 1975. 808 pp. [3rd ed. *in press*] (069 REF) [257]

KLOSTER (G.B.) Handbuch der Museen. Deutschland BRD, DDR, Österreich, Schweiz. Pullach (Munich): Verlag Dokumentation, 1971. 2 vol. (069 REF) [258]

HUDSON (Kenneth) A guide to the industrial archaeology of Europe. Bath: Adams and Dart, 1971. 186 pp. (6:93) [259]

EVANS (Hilary) *and* EVANS (Mary), *Eds.* The picture researcher's handbook: an international guide to picture sources – and how to use them. 2nd ed. London: Saturday Ventures, 1979. 328 pp. (084) [260]

b. Great Britain

PHILIP (A.J.) An index to the special collections in libraries, museums and art galleries (public, private and official) in Great Britain and Ireland. London: F.G. Brown, 1949. 190 pp. (02 REF) [262]

LIBRARIES, MUSEUMS AND ART GALLERIES YEARBOOK 1978–79. Edited by Adrian Brink. Cambridge: James Clarke, 1981. [Not paginated] (02REF) [263]

MUSEUMS ASSOCIATION. Museums yearbook including a directory of museums and galleries of the British Isles and an index to their administering authorities. London. [Annual] (069 REF) [264]

MUSEUMS AND ART GALLERIES IN GREAT BRITAIN AND IRELAND 1978. Dunstable, Beds.: ABC Historic Publns., 1980? 115 pp. (069 REF and 084) [265]

SMART (J.E.) Museums in Great Britain with scientific and technological collections: a list. 2nd ed. London: Science Museum, 1978. 88 pp. (069 REF) [266]

WALL (John) Directory of British photographic collections. London: Heinemann, 1977. 226 pp. (02 REF) [267]

WISE (Terence), *Comp.* A guide to military museums. 2nd rev. ed. Hemel Hempstead, Herts.: Model and Allied Publns., 1971. 31 pp. (069 REF) [268]

c. France

BARNAUD (G.) Répertoire des musées de France et de la Communauté. (Direction des Musées de France). Paris, 1959. 416 pp. [269]

d. Germany

JEDDING (H.) Keysers Führer durch Museen und Sammlungen. Bundesrepublik und West Berlin. Heidelberg: Keyserche Verlag, 1961. 558 pp. [270]

GOLDBECK (G.) Technische Museen. Führer zu den Museen für die Geschichte von Naturwissenschaft, Technik, Gewerbe und Industrie in der Bundesrepublik Deutschland und West-Berlin. (Museen in Deutschland (West)). Stuttgart: J. Fink, 1975. 70 pp. (069 REF) [271]

DER DEUTSCHE MUSEUMSFÜHRER. Frankfurt-on--Main: Wolfgang Kruger Verlag, 1979. 789 pp. [Covers some 1,500 museums in West Germany and West Berlin] (069 REF) [271A]

e. United States and Canada

THE OFFICIAL MUSEUM DIRECTORY 1981. United States. Canada. (The American Association of Museums). Skokie, Ill.: National Register Publishing Co., 1980. 1088 pp. (069 REF) [272]

[*See also* Directories, 969–981A]

XI. INTERNATIONAL EXHIBITIONS.

DILKE (C.W.) Exhibition of the works of industry of all nations, 1851. Catalogue of a collection of works on or having reference to the Exhibition of 1851. London, 1855. 116 pp. (017:061.4) [273]

BLAKE (William P.) Bibliography of the Paris Universal Exhibition of 1867. *Reports of the United States Commissioners to the Paris Universal Exposition, 1867.* Washington, 1870. Vol. 1. 39 pp. (British Library AS 408/11) [274]

INTERNATIONAL EXHIBITIONS, 1851–1907. *Journal, Royal Society of Arts*, 55 (1907), 1140-1146. (TL8374) [275]

MANDELL (Richard D.) Paris 1900. The great world's fair. Toronto: Univ. of Toronto Press., 1967. 173 pp. [Contains bibliographies of the 1900 and other exhibitions] [276]

ALTICK (R.D.) The shows of London. A panoramic history of exhibitions, 1600–1862. Cambridge, Mass.: Belknap Pr., 1978. 553 pp. (061.4:93) [277]

XII. INTERNATIONAL CONGRESSES OF THE HISTORY OF SCIENCE

1st CONGRESS, PARIS 1929. Comptes rendus de la première session du Comité Internationale d'Histoire des Sciences et du premier Congrès . . . *Archeion*, 11 (1929), suppl., I–CXI [278]

2nd CONGRESS, LONDON 1931. [Committees and provisional timetable. Summary of proceedings. Papers and notes.] *Archeion*, 13 (1931), 74-76, 157-167, 296-299, 471-490, 493-494; 14 (1932), 106, 271-288, 496-534. [See also *Isis*, 16 (1931), 126-129] [279]

———————— Science at the crossroads: papers presented to the [2nd] International Congress . . . by the delegates of the U.S.S.R. 2nd ed. London: Frank Cass and Co., 1971. 235 pp. [280]

3rd CONGRESS, COIMBRA 1934. 3e Congrès . . . Actes, conférences et communications. Lisbon, 1936. 463 pp. [See also *Archeion*, 16 (1934), 100-102, 337-372; *Isis*, 28 (1938), 135-138] [281]

4th CONGRESS, PRAGUE 1937. [Proceedings of the 4th . . . congress . . . , Prague, 1937] *Acta historiae rerum naturalium necnon technicarum*, special issue 6 (1973). 389 pp. [See also *Archeion*, 19 (1937), 374-376, 401; *Isis*, 26 (1937), 452-453] [282]

5th CONGRESS, LAUSANNE 1947. Actes du 5e Congrès . . . (Collection de travaux de l'Académie Internationale d'Histoire des Sciences, no. 2). Paris: Hermann, 1948. 288 pp. [See also *Arch. int. hist. sci.*, 1 (1948), 312, 332-335; *Isis*, 39 (1948), 65-66] [283]

6th CONGRESS, AMSTERDAM 1950. Actes de 6e Congrès . . . (Collection de travaux de l'Académie Internationale d'Histoire des Sciences, no. 6). Paris: Hermann, 1951-1953. 1 vol. in 2. 723 pp. [See also *Arch. int. hist. sci.*, 4 (1951), 135-172; *Isis*, 42 (1951), 45] [284]

7th CONGRESS, JERUSALEM 1953. Actes du 7e Congrès . . . (Collection de travaux de l'Académie Internationale d'Histoire des Sciences, no. 8). Paris: Hermann, 1954. 644 pp. [See also *Arch. int. hist. sci.*, 6 (1953), 453-479; *Isis*, 45 (1954), 63-77; *Vop. ist. est. tekh.*, 2 (1956), 294-297] [285]

8th CONGRESS, FLORENCE – MILAN 1956. Actes du 8e Congrès . . . (Collection de travaux de l'Académie Internationale d'Histoire des Sciences, no. 9). Paris: Hermann, 1958. 3 vol. in 2. 1224 pp. [See also *Arch. int. hist. sci.*, 11 (1958), 43-44; *Isis*, 48 (1957), 176-181] [286]

9th CONGRESS, BARCELONA – MADRID 1959. 9 Congreso Internacional de Historia de la Ciencias, . . . n.p., 1959–60. 3 pt. [287]

———————— Actes du 9e Congrès . . . . (Collection de travaux de l'Académie International d'Histoire des Sciences, no. 12). Paris: Hermann, 1960. 2 vol. 732 pp. [See also *Arch. int. hist. sci.*, 12 (1959), 225-252] [288]

10th CONGRESS, ITHACA 1962. Actes du dixième Congrès . . . (Collection de travaux de l'Académie Internationale d'Histoire des Sciences, no. 15). Paris: Hermann, 1964. 1 vol. in 2. 1058 pp. [See also *Arch. int. hist. sci.*, 15 (1962), 365-407; *Sterne*, 39 (1963), 200-204] [289]

11th CONGRESS, WARSAW 1965. 11e Congrès . . . Programme. Warsaw, 1965. 84 pp. [290]

———————— 11e Congrès . . . Sommaires. Warsaw, 1965. 594 pp. [291]

———————— Actes . . . (Académie Polonaise des Sciences, Institut d'Histoire de la Science et de la Technique). Wroclaw: Ossolineum, 1967–1968. 6 vol. [See also *Arch. int. hist. sci.*, 21 (1968), 273-276] [292]

12th CONGRESS, PARIS 1968. 12e Congrès . . . Resumés des communications. Summaries. Paris, 1968. 258 pp.[293]

———————— Colloques, textes et rapports. (*Revue de synthèse*, 3e sér., no. 49-52). Paris: Albin Michel, 1968. 431 pp. [294]

———————— Actes. Paris: Albert Blanchard, 1970–71. 12 vol. [295]

13th CONGRESS, MOSCOW 1971. Trudy . . . kongressa . . . Moskcow Izdatel'stvo "Nauka", 1974. 13 vol. [296]

14th CONGRESS, TOKYO 1974. Proceedings . . . Tokyo: Science Council of Japan, 1974–75. 4 vol. [See also *Arch. int. hist. sci.*, 25 (1975), 100-101] [297]

15th CONGRESS, EDINBURGH 1977. Human implications of scientific advance. Proceedings of the . . . Congress . . . Edited by E.G. Forbes. Edinburgh: Univ. Pr., 1978. 596 pp. [298]

16th CONGRESS, BUCHAREST 1981. Proceedings. Bucharest: Academy of the Socialist Republic of Romania, 1981. 4 vol. [298A]

(Science Museum Library's holdings: Congress proceedings published separately are shelved at 93 TE 865; other shelf-marks are: *Archeion* 93 JA 793; *Archives internationales d'histoire des sciences* 93 JA 793; *Isis* 93 JI 94; *Acta historiae rerum naturalium* . . . 93 JS 0941; *Revue de synthèse* 0 JR 629; *Voprosy istorii estestvoznaniya i tekhniki* 93 JV 873)

XIII. HISTORIANS OF SCIENCE

INTERNATIONAL COMMISSION ON HISTORY OF MATHEMATICS. World directory of historians of mathematics. 2nd ed. by Kenneth O. May and Laura Roebuck. Toronto, 1978. 92 pp. (93JW931) [299]

CLARK (P.K.) *and* CAMPBELL (E.M.J.) International directory of current research in the history of cartography and in carto-bibliography. London: privately published, 1976. 88 pp. [Continued as a serial, no. 3 (1981), by the Geography Dept. of Birkbeck College, London] (93JI729) [300]

HISTORY OF SCIENCE SOCIETY. ISIS guide to the history of science. 5th ed. Washington, 1980. 168 pp. [Contains: Guide to graduate study and research; Guide to scholarly journals publishing articles in the history of science; Directory of members] (93JI94) [301]

JAYAWARDENE (S.A.) *and* LAWES (J.) Biographical notices of historians of science: a checklist. *Annals of science*, 36 (1979), 315-394. [Bibliography of some 3,000 notices (800 historians of science) including obituary notices, bibliographies, articles in biographical dictionaries, and monographs] (93JA458) [302]

COSTABEL (P.) *and* GRMEK (M.D.) L'Académie Internationale d'Histoire des Sciences: cinquante ans, 1927–1977. Paris: Vrin, 1978. 121 pp. (93TP0987) [302A]

PART II

History and Related Subjects

[303 - 665]

XIV. GUIDES FOR RESEARCH

BARZUN (J.) *and* GRAFF (H.F.) The modern researcher. Rev. ed. New York: Harcourt Brace Jovanovich, 1977. 378 pp. [On the techniques of research and the art of expression] (001.8) [303]

KITSON CLARK (G.) Guide for research students working on historical subjects. 2nd ed. Cambridge: Univ. Pr., 1969. 64 pp. [By a Cambridge historian for students starting research] (93) [304]

WATSON (George) The literary thesis: a guide to research. London: Longman, 1970. 188 pp. [Advice to graduate students undertaking literary research for a higher degree from a teacher/researcher. Part 2 (pp. 79–188, Aids to research) is a collection of essays by experts (subjects include: techniques of textual criticism; history of Western MSS; presentation of articles for publication)] (001.8) [305]

McCOY (F.M.) Researching and writing history. A practical handbook for students. Berkeley: Univ. of California Pr., 1974. 128 pp. ["Step-by-step guide to the preparation of a research paper, from selecting a working topic to editing the final draft." Provides guidance not generally found in handbooks on writing theses and term papers] [306]

HOFFMANN (Ann) Research: [a handbook for writers and journalists]. 2nd ed. London: A. & C. Black, 1979. 148 pp. [Guide for free-lance writers by a professional researcher. Contains a wealth of information and practical advice of use to the student-historian] [307]

XV. HISTORICAL METHODS

LANGLOIS (C.V.) *and* SEIGNOBOS (C.) Introduction to the study of history. 4th impression. London: Duckworth, 1926. 350 pp. [First published 1898. Reprinted by Frank Cass 1966] [308]

MARSHALL (R.L.) The historical criticism of documents. London: S.P.C.K., 1920. 62 pp. (Helps for students of history, 28) (SML) [309]

GOTTSCHALK (L.R.) Understanding history: a primer of historical method. 2nd ed. New York: Knopf, 1969. 310 pp. [310]

SAMARAN (C.) L'histoire et ses méthodes. Paris: Gallimard, 1961. 1772 pp. (Encyclopédie de la Pléiade, 11) (93) [311]

GALBRAITH (V.H.) An introduction to the study of history. London: C.A. Watts, 1964. 143 pp. [312]

BRANDT (A. von) Werkzeug des Historikers. Eine Einführung in die historischen Hilfswissenschaften. 8. Auflage. Stuttgart: Kohlhammer, 1976? 206 pp. (Urban Taschenbuch 33) (93) [314]

XVI. HISTORY: REFERENCE BOOKS AND BIBLIOGRAPHIES

1. *Guides*
2. *Current Bibliographies*
3. *Other Reference Books*
4. *Historical Periodicals*

1. *Guides*

LANGLOIS (C.V.) Manuel de la bibliographie historique. Paris: Hachette, 1901–1904. 2 vol. 623 pp. [Reprinted Graz, 1968] [315]

DUTCHER (G.M.) *and others.* A guide to historical literature. Edited by W.H. Allison, S.B. Fay, A.H. Shearer and H.R. Shipman. New York: Macmillan, 1931. 1222 pp. [316]

COULTER (E.M.) *and* GERSTENFELD (M.) Historical bibliographies: a systematic and annotated guide. Berkeley, Calif.: Univ. of California Pr., 1935. 206 pp. [317]

INSTITUTE OF HISTORICAL RESEARCH, UNIVERSITY OF LONDON. Bibliography of historical works issued in the United Kingdom, 1946/56 – 1966/70. Eds., J.C. Lancaster, W. Kellaway. London: 1957–72. 4 vol. (Compiled for the Anglo-American Conference of Historians) (016:93) [318]

AMERICAN HISTORICAL ASSOCIATION. Guide to historical literature. New York: Macmillan, 1961. 962 pp. (016:93) [319]

WYNAR (L.R.) History: a selective and annotated bibliographical guide. Boulder, Colo.: Univ. of Colorado, Social Science Library, 1963. 348 pp. [320]

HEPWORTH (P.) How to find out in history: a guide to sources of information for all. Oxford: Pergamon, 1966. 242 pp. (016:93) [321]

HARVARD UNIVERSITY LIBRARY. Widener Library shelflist 32. General European and world history classification schedule, classified listing by call number, chronological listing, author and title listing. Cambridge, Mass., 1970. 959 pp. [322]

POULTON (H.J.) The historian's handbook: a descriptive guide to reference works. Norman: Univ. of Oklahoma Pr., 1972. 304 pp. (016:93) [323]

CHALONER (W.H.) *and* RICHARDSON (R.C.) British economic and social history. A bibliographical guide. Manchester: Manchester Univ. Pr., 1976. 130 pp. [324]

CHADWICK (Owen) The history of the Church: a select bibliography. Rev. ed. London: Historical Assn., 1973. 52 pp. (Helps for students of history, 66) [324A]

2. *Current Bibliographies*

INTERNATIONAL BIBLIOGRAPHY OF THE HISTORICAL SCIENCES, 1 (1926)+ Paris: Armand Colin, 1930+ [325]

HISTORICAL ASSOCIATION, LONDON. Annual bulletin of historical literature. Publications of the year 1911+ London, 1912+ [326]

BIBLIOGRAPHIE ANNUELLE DE L'HISTOIRE DE FRANCE du cinquième siècle à 1939. Année 1955+ Paris: CNRS, 1956+ [327]

3. Other Reference Books

MULLINS (E.L.C.) Texts and calendars: an analytical guide to serial publications. London: Royal Historical Society, 1958. 674 pp. (Guides and handbooks, no. 7) [328]

WHO'S WHO IN HISTORY. General ed., C.R.N. Routh. Oxford: Blackwell, 1960–69. 5 vol. [329]

LANGER (W.L.) An encyclopedia of world history. 5th ed. Boston: Houghton, 1972. 1569 pp. (930.9) [330]

HOWAT (G.M.D.) Dictionary of world history. General editor: G.M.D. Howat. Advisory editor: A.J.P. Taylor. London: Nelson, 1973. 1720 pp. [331]

CROSS (F.L.), *Ed.* The Oxford dictionary of the Christian Church. 2nd ed., by F.L. Cross and E.A. Livingstone. London: Oxford Univ. Pr., 1974. 1518 pp. [332]

ENCICLOPEDIA CATTOLICA. Vatican City, 1949–53. 12 vol. [More recent than the *Catholic encyclopaedia* (New York, 1907–14), 16 vol.] [333]

4. Historical Periodicals

KRAMM (H.) Bibliographie historischer Zeitschriften, 1939–1951. Marburg: Rasch, 1952–54. 3 vol. [334]

CARON (P.) *and* JARYC (M.) Liste mondiale des périodiques et bibliographies historiques. Oxford: International Committee of Historical Sciences, 1939. 405 pp. [335]

BOEHM (E.H.) *and* ADOLPHUS (L.) Historical periodicals. An annotated world list of historical and related serial publications. Santa Barbara, Calif.: Clio Press, 1961. 618 pp. [336]

KIRBY (J.L.) A guide to historical periodicals in the English language. London: Historical Assn., 1970. 48 pp. (Helps for students of history, 80) [337]

XVII. ANTIQUITY

1. Guides

LAURAND (L.) *and* LAURAS (A.) Manuel des études grecques et latines. 14e éd. Paris: Picard, 1966–68. 2 vol. [338]

PETIT (P.) Guide de l'étudiant en histoire ancienne. 3e éd. Paris: Presses Univ. de France, 1969. 239 pp. (016:931) [339]

2. Encyclopedias and Dictionaries

PAULY (A.F. von) *and* WISSOWA (G.) Pauly's Real-encyclopädie der classischen Altertumswissenschaft. Neue Bearb. hrsg. von Wilhelm Kroll und Karl Mittelhaus. Stuttgart: Metzlerscher, 1894–1978. 49 vol. in 83.
----- ----- Register der Nachträge und Supplementen von Hans Gartner und Albert Wunsch. Munich: Alfred Druckenmüller, 1980. 250 pp. [Generally known as *Pauly-Wissowa.* Published in two series with supplements and index. Standard reference work; extensive bibliographies. Updated by 342] (Warburg Institute) [340]

DAREMBERG (C.) *and* SAGLIO (E.) Dictionnaire des antiquités grecques et romaines. Paris: Hachette, 1873–1919. 6 vol. [341]

DER KLEINE PAULY. Lexikon der Antike. Auf der Grundlage von Pauly's Realencyclopädie der classischen Altertumswissenschaft. Ed. Konrad Ziegler, Walther

Sontheimer. Stuttgart: Druckenmüller, 1964–75. 5 vol. (937/938) [342]

ANDRESEN (Carl) *and others.* Lexikon der alten Welt. Zurich: Artemis, 1965. 3524 col. [343]

OXFORD CLASSICAL DICTIONARY. 2nd ed. by N.G.L. Hammond and H.H. Scullard. Oxford: Clarendon Pr., 1970. 1176 pp. (937/938) [344]

3. Bibliographies

JAHRESBERICHT ÜBER DIE FORTSCHRITTE DER CLASSISCHEN ALTERTUMSWISSENSCHAFT. Begr. von C. Bursian. Leipzig (Göttingen), 1873–1945/55. 285 vol. [Continuation in: *Lustrum: internationale Forschungsberichte aus dem Bereich des klassischen Altertums,* 1 (1956)+ Göttingen, 1957+] [345]

ENGELMANN (W.) Bibliotheca scriptorum classicorum. 8. Auflage umfassend die Literatur von 1700 bis 1878. Leipzig: Engelmann, 1880–82. 2 vol. [346]

HANDBUCH DER ALTERTUMSWISSENSCHAFT. Begr. von Iwan von Müller. Munich: Beck, 1885+ [*In progress.* This "magistrale synthèse collective allemande" consists of handbooks (frequently updated) to the various disciplines and areas relevant to the study of antiquity (including Byzantium and the Middle Ages). Some 60 volumes already published. Details in Malclès (680), vol. 2, pp. 105-106; in Walford (682), vol. 2, p. 481; and in *VLB* 1979/80 (739)] [347]

L'ANNÉE PHILOLOGIQUE. Bibliographie critique et analytique de l'antiquité gréco-latine. Paris, Belles-Lettres, 1928+ [Annual] [348]

KRISTELLER (P.O.) Catalogus translationum et commentariorum: mediaeval and Renaissance Latin translations and commentaries. Annotated lists and guides. Washington, D.C.: Catholic Univ. of America Pr., 1960–80. 4 vol. (016:8.03) [349]

ROUNDS (D.) Articles on antiquity in *Festschriften*. The ancient near East, the Old Testament, Greece, Rome, Roman Law, Byzantium. An index. Cambridge, Mass.: Harvard Univ. Pr., 1962. 560 pp. [350]

PARKS (G.B.) *and* TEMPLE (R.Z.) The literatures of the world in English translation. A bibliography. Vol. 1. The Greek and Latin literatures. New York: Ungar, 1968. 442 pp. [351]

BORGER (R.) Handbuch der Keilschriftenliteratur. Berlin: De Gruyter, 1967–1975. 3 vol. [Subject index in vol. 3] [352]

XVIII. THE MIDDLE AGES. BYZANTIUM

HALPHEN (D.) *and* RENOUARD (Y.) Initiation aux études d'histoire du moyen âge. Paris: Presses Universitaires de France, 1952. 105 pp. [353]

PAETOW (L.J.) Guide to the study of medieval history. New York: Crofts, 1931. 643 pp. [Reprinted 1959. For suppl., *see* 360A] (016:940.1) [354]

CAENEGEM (R.C. van) Guide to the sources of medieval history. With the collaboration of F.L. Ganshof. Amsterdam: North Holland Publishing Co., 1978. 428 pp. (016:940.1) [355]

DAVIS (R.H.C.) Medieval European history, 395–1500. A select bibliography. 2nd ed. London: Historical Assn., 1968. 48 pp. [356]

WILLIAMS (H.F.) An index of medieval studies published in *Festschriften,* 1865–1946, with special reference to Romanic material. Berkeley: Univ. of California Pr., 1951. 165 pp. [357]

GRAVES (E.B.), *Ed.* A bibliography of English history to 1485: based on "The sources and literature of English history from the earliest times to about 1485" by Charles Gross. Oxford: Oxford Univ. Pr., 1975. 1103 pp. [358]

KRUMBACHER (K.) Geschichte der byzantinischen Literatur von Justinian bis zum Ende des oströmischen Reiches (527–1453). 2. Aufl. Munich: Beck, 1897. 1193 pp. (Handbuch der klassischen Altertumswissenschaft 9.1) [359]

BYZANTINISCHE ZEITSCHRIFT. Munich, 1892+ [Contains a current bibliography] [360]

BOYCE (G.C.), *Ed.* and *comp.* Literature of medieval history, 1930–1975. A supplement to Louis John Paetow's "A guide to the study of medieval history." New York: Kraus, 1981. 5 vol. [Bibliography of some 55,000 works classified under more than 3,000 headings, covering the period 500–1500. Detailed indexes] [360A]

XIX. SLAVONIC STUDIES

HORECKY (L.) Basic Russian publications. An annotated bibliography on Russia and the Soviet Union. Chicago: Univ. of Chicago Pr., 1962. 313 pp. (016:908(47)) [361]

HORECKY (L.) Russia and the Soviet Union. A bibliographic guide to Western-language publications. Chicago: Univ. of Chicago Pr., 1965. 473 pp. (016:908(47)) [362]

SIMMONS (J.S.G.) Russian bibliography, libraries and archives: a selective list of bibliographical references for students of Russian history, literature, political, social and philosophical thought, theology and linguistics. Oxford: privately published, 1973. 76 pp. [363]

KIRIPIČEVA (I.K.) Handbuch der russischen und sowjetischen Bibliographien. Die allgemeine Bibliographien, Fachbibliographien und Nachschlagwerke Russlands und der Sowjetunion. Leipzig: VEB Verlag, 1962. 225 pp. [364]

WALKER (Gregory) Directory of libraries and special collections on Eastern Europe and the USSR. London: Crosby, Lockwood, 1971. 159 pp. (02 REF) [365]

XX. THE ORIENT

1. *Bibliographical Guides*
2. *Special Libraries*
3. *The Middle East*
4. *India*
5. *East Asia*

1. *Bibliographical Guides*

PEARSON (J.D.) Oriental and Asian bibliography. An introduction with some references to Africa. Bombay: W.D. Willis, 1966. 261 pp. [366]

NUNN (G.R.) Asia: reference works; a select annotated guide. London: Mansell, 1980. 365 pp. [Much enlarged version of Nunn's *Asia: a selected and annotated guide* (1971)] [367]

BESTERMAN (T.) A world bibliography of Oriental bibliographies. Revised, and brought up to date by J.D. Pearson. Oxford: Basil Blackwell, 1975. 727 col. [Based on 673] [368]

PHILIPS (C.H.), *Ed.* Handbook of Oriental history. London: Royal Historical Society, 1951. 265 pp. [369]

2. *Special Libraries*

PEARSON (J.D.) Oriental manuscript collections in the libraries of Great Britain and Ireland. London: Royal Asiatic Society, 1954. 90 pp. [370]

PEARSON (J.D.) Oriental manuscripts in Europe and North America. A survey. Zug: Inter Documentation Company, 1971. 515 pp. (Bibliotheca Asiatica 7) [371]

COLLISON (R.L.W.) Directory of libraries and special collections on Asia and North Africa. London: Crosby, Lockwood, 1970. 123 pp. [372]

BRITISH MUSEUM. The catalogues of the Oriental printed books and manuscripts. By F.C. Francis. Rev. ed. London, 1959. 15 pp. [Originally published in *Journal of documentation*, 7 (1951), 170-187] (02TL1774) [373]

BRITISH LIBRARY. Guide to the Department of Oriental Manuscripts and Printed Books. By H.J. Goodacre and A.P. Pritchard. London, 1977. 72 pp. (026:091) [374]

3. The Middle East

GABRIELI (G.) Manuale di bibliografia musulmana. Parte prima. Bibliografia generale. Rome, 1916. 491 pp. [375]

GRIMWOOD-JONES (D.), HOPWOOD (D.) *and* PEARSON (J.D.) Arab Islamic bibliography: the Middle East Library Committee guide; based on Giuseppe Gabrieli's *Manuale di bibliografia musulmana*. Hassocks, Sussex: Harvester Pr., 1977. 292 pp. [376]

ETTINGHAUSEN (R.), *Ed.* A selected and annotated bibliography of books and periodicals in Western languages dealing with the Near and Middle East; with special emphasis on medieval and modern times. With suppl. Washington: Middle East Institute, 1954. 137 pp. [377]

al-HAJRASI (Sa'ad M.) Bibliographical guide to reference works in the Arab world. Guide bibliographique des ouvrages de référence dans le monde arabe. Cairo, 1965. 130 pp. (Issued in co-operation with UNESCO) [378]

SAUVAGET (Jean) Introduction to the history of the Muslim East. A bibliographical guide. Based on the second edition as recast by Claude Cohen. Berkeley and Los Angeles: Univ. of California Pr., 1965. 252 pp. [379]

HOPWOOD (D.) *and* GRIMWOOD-JONES (D.), *Eds.* Middle East and Islam. A bibliographical introduction. Zug, Switzerland: Inter Documentation, 1972. 368 pp. (Bibliotheca Asiatica 9) [380]

LITTLEFIELD (D.W.) The Islamic Near East and North Africa. An annotated guide to books in English for non-specialists. Littleton, Colo.: Libraries Unlimited, 1977. 375 pp. [381]

SEZGIN (F.) Geschichte des arabischen Schrifttums. Leyden: Brill, 1967–79. 7 vol. [Vol. 1: Manuscript collections; Vol. 3: Medicine, pharmacy, zoology; Vol. 4: Alchemy, chemistry, botany; Vol. 5: Mathematics; Vol. 6: Astronomy; Vol. 7: Astrology. *In progress*] (5(5):93) [382]

ARNOLD (*Sir* T.W.) *and* GUILLAUME (A.) The legacy of Islam. Ed. by Joseph Schacht with C.E. Bosworth. 2nd ed. Oxford: Clarendon Pr., 1974. 530 pp. (93) [383]

ENCYCLOPAEDIA OF ISLAM. New ed. London: Brill, 1960–78. [4 vol. (out of 5). *In progress.* First ed., 1911–38, 4 vol., suppl. There is a companion atlas edited by W.C. Brice: *An historical atlas of Islam* (Leiden: Brill, 1981), 71 pp. (SML)] (03) [384]

SHUNAMI (Shlomo) Bibliography of Jewish bibliographies. 2nd ed. Jerusalem: The Hebrew University, 1965. 992 pp. Suppl., 1975. 464 pp. [385]

ENCYCLOPAEDIA JUDAICA. New York: Macmillan, 1972. 16 vol. (VAL) [386]

4. *India*

PATIL (H.S.) *and* RANI (B.), *Eds.* History and culture. Select bibliographies. Delhi: Indian Council for Cultural Relations, 1971. 216 pp. [387]

SHARMA (H.D.), MUKHERJI (S.P.) *and* SINGH (L.M.P.) Indian reference sources. An annotated guide to Indian reference books. Jullundur: Indian Bibliographic Centre, 1972. 313 pp. [388]

SHARMA (J.S.) Sources of Indian civilization. A bibliography of works by world orientalists other than Indian. Delhi: Vikas, 1974. 360 pp. [389]

BASHAM (A.L.), *Ed.* A cultural history of India. Oxford: Clarendon Pr., 1975. 585 pp. [Revision of G.T. Garratt, *Legacy of India* (1937)] [390]

5. *East Asia*

GILLIN (D.), EHRMAN (E.) *and* MOREHOUSE (W.) East Asia: a bibliography for undergraduate libraries. Williamsport, Pa.: Bro-dart Publishing Co., 1970. 130 pp. [391]

TSIEN (Tsuen-hsuin) China: an annotated bibliography of bibliographies. Compiled in collaboration with J.K.M. Cheng. Boston, Mass.: G.K. Hall, 1978. 604 pp. [391A]

HUCKER (C.O.) China: a critical bibliography. Tucson: Univ. of Arizona Pr., 1962. 126 pp. [392]

TENG SSU-YÜ *and* BIGGERSTAFF (K.) Annotated bibliography of selected Chinese reference works. 3rd ed. Cambridge: Harvard Univ. Pr., 1971. 250 pp. (Harvard-Yenching Institute Studies, 2) [Provides Western students of Sinology with an elementary guide to the most important reference works] [393]

XXI. MODERN HISTORY

GUIRAL (P.), PILLORGET (R.) *and* AGULHON (M.) Guide de l'étudiant en histoire moderne et contemporaine. Paris: Presses Univ. de France, 1971. 333 pp. [394]

ROACH (J.), *Ed.* A bibliography of modern history. Cambridge: Cambridge Univ. Pr., 1968. 388 pp. [395]

ANNUAL REGISTER OF WORLD EVENTS: a review of public events at home and abroad for the year 1758+ London, 1761+ (JA 59) [396]

———————— General index to Dodsley's *Annual register*, 1758 to 1819. London: Baldwin, 1826. 938 pp. (JA59) [397]

HISTORICAL ABSTRACTS, 1775–1945. Vol. 1+ New York, 1955+ [Since 1973 coverage is from 1450 to 1964] (016:93) [398]

WILLIAMS (J.B.) A guide to the printed materials for English social and economic history 1750–1850. New York: Columbia Univ. Pr., 1926. 2 vol. [Reprinted 1966 by Octagon Books, New York] (016:93) [399]

WILSON (Charles) *and* PARKER (Geoffrey) An introduction to the sources of European economic history, 1500–1800. London: Weidenfeld & Nicolson, 1977. 265 pp. [400]

READ (Conyers) Bibliography of British history. Tudor period, 1485–1603. 2nd ed. Oxford: Clarendon Pr., 1959. 624 pp. [401]

DAVIES (Godfrey) Bibliography of British history. Stuart period, 1603–1714. 2nd ed. by M.F. Keeler. Oxford: Clarendon Pr., 1970. 734 pp. [402]

PARGELLIS (S.) *and* MEDLEY (D.J.) Bibliography of British history. The eighteenth century, 1714–1789. Oxford: Clarendon Pr., 1951. 642 pp. [403]

BROWN (Lucy M.) *and* CHRISTIE (Ian R.) Bibliography of British history, 1789–1851. Oxford: Clarendon Pr., 1977. 759 pp. [404]

HANHAM (H.J.) Bibliography of British history, 1851–1914. Oxford: Clarendon Pr., 1976. 1606 pp. [405]

XXII. BRITISH LOCAL HISTORY

1. *Manuals*
2. *Guides to Sources*
3. *Bibliographies*
4. *Maps*
5. *County Histories*

1. Manuals

PUGH (R.B.) How to write a parish history. 6th ed. London: George Allen and Unwin Ltd., 1954. 148 pp. [First published 1879] [406]

HOSKINS (W.G.) Local history in England. 2nd ed. London: Longman, 1972. 268 pp. [407]

IREDALE (D.) Local history research and writing: a manual for local history writers. Leeds: Elmfield Pr., 1974. 225 pp. [408]

RICHARDSON (John) Local historian's encyclopedia. London: Historical Publications, 1974. 312 pp. [408A]

GOODER (Eileen) Latin for local history. An introduction. 2nd ed. London: Longman, 1978. 171 pp. (807.1) [409]

STANDING CONFERENCE FOR LOCAL HISTORY. Local history societies in England and Wales: a list. London, 1978. 34 pp. [410]

2. Guides to Sources

KUHLICKE (F.W.) *and* EMMISON (F.G.), *Eds.* The English local history handlist: a short bibliography and list of sources for the study of local history and antiquities. Rev. ed. London: Historical Assn., 1969. 84 pp. [411]

STEPHENS (W.B.) Sources for English local history. Rev. ed. Cambridge: Cambridge Univ. Pr., 1981. 342 pp. (016:93(410)) [412]

EMMISON (F.G.) *and* SMITH (W.J.) Material for theses in some local record offices. London: Phillimore, 1973. 44 pp. [413]

3. Bibliographies

GROSS (C.) A bibliography of British municipal history; including guilds and parliamentary representation. 2nd ed. by G.H. Martin. Leicester: Univ. Pr., 1966. 461 pp. (016:93) [414]

HUMPHREYS (A.L.) A handbook to county bibliography: being a bibliography of bibliographies relating to the county towns of Great Britain and Ireland. London: Dawsons, 1974. 501 pp. [Reprint of the 1917 ed.] (016:93(410)) [415]

MARTIN (G.H.) *and* McINTYRE (S.) A bibliography of British and Irish municipal history. Volume I. General works. Leicester: Univ. Pr., 1972. 806 pp. [416]

4. Maps

ANDERSON (John P.) The book of British topography. A classified catalogue of the topographical works in the library of the British Museum relating to Great Britain and Ireland. London: W. Satchell, 1881. 472 pp. [417]

HARLEY (J.B.) *and* PHILLIPS (C.W.) The historian's guide to Ordnance Survey maps. London: National Council of Social Service, 1964. 51 pp. (528.9:93) [418]

HARLEY (J.B.) Maps for the local historian. A guide to the British sources. (Reprinted from *The Local historian*). London: National Council of Social Service, 1972. 86 pp. [419]

BARLEY (M.W.) A guide to British topographical collections. London: Council for British Archaeology, 1974. 159 pp. (016:914.10) [420]

5. County Histories

VICTORIA HISTORY OF THE COUNTIES OF ENGLAND. A guide to the Victoria History of the Counties of England. By H. Arthur Doubleday and William Page. London: Archibald Constable, 1912. 140 pp. [Intended for contributors] [421]

VICTORIA HISTORY OF THE COUNTIES OF ENGLAND. Eds., H.A. Doubleday and W. Page. London: Constable; Oxford Univ. Pr., 1901+ [For details, *see* Walford, vol. 2 (682), or Sheehy (687)] (942) [422]

VICTORIA HISTORY OF THE COUNTIES OF ENGLAND. General introduction. *Ed.* by R.B. Pugh. London: 1970. 282 pp. [423]

XXIII. HISTORY OF EDUCATION

1. *General*
2. *Universities*
   a. *Europe*
   b. *Great Britain and Ireland*
   c. *Germany*

1. *General*

WATSON (Foster) The encyclopaedia and dictionary of education. London: Pitman, 1921–22. 4 vols. [424]

BOYD (William) The history of Western education. 6th ed. London: Adam and Charles Black, 1975. 517 pp. [First published 1921] [425]

HIGSON (C.W.J.) Sources for the history of education. A list of materials (including school books) contained in the Libraries of the Institutes and Schools of Education together with works from the Libraries of the Universities of Nottingham and Reading. London: Library Assn., 1967. 196 pp. Suppl. 1965–74. 1976. 221 pp. [426]

HARVARD UNIVERSITY LIBRARY. Widener Library shelflists 16-17. Education. Cambridge, Mass., 1968. 2 vol. [427]

HISTORY OF EDUCATION SOCIETY, LANCASTER. Guide to sources in the history of education, 1 (1971)+ (016:93:37) [428]

BOWEN (James) A history of Western education. London: Methuen, 1972–1975. 2 vol. [From 2000 B.C. to the 16th century] (37:93) [429]

2. Universities

a. Europe

AIGRAIN (R.) Histoire des universités. Paris: Presses Univ. de France, 1949. 127 pp. (Que sais-je? No. 391) [429A]

RASHDALL (H.) The universities of Europe in the Middle Ages. 2nd ed. by F.M. Powicke and A.B. Emden. Oxford: Clarendon Pr., 1936. 3 vol. (378:93) [430]

COMMISSION INTERNATIONALE POUR L'HISTOIRE DES UNIVERSITÉS. Bibliographie internationale de l'histoire des universités. Geneva: Droz, 1973+ [*In progress*] (016:93:37) [431]

IRSAY (Stephen d') Histoire des universités françaises et étrangères des origines à nos jours. Paris: Picard, 1933–35. 2 vol. (378:93) [432]

b. Great Britain and Ireland

GABRIEL (A.L.), *Ed.* Summary bibliography of the history of the universities of Great Britain and Ireland up to 1800, covering publications between 1900 and 1968. Notre Dame, Ind.: Univ. of Notre Dame, Mediaeval Inst., 1974. 154 pp. (016:93:37) [433]

WALLIS (P.J.) Histories of old schools: a revised list for England and Wales. Newcastle upon Tyne: The University, Department of Education, 1966. 98 pp. [Select bibliography of the history of the schools which existed in England and Wales before 1700] [434]

JACOBS (P.M.) Registers of the universities, colleges and schools of Great Britain and Ireland: a list. London: Inst. of Historical Research, 1964. 50 pp. [435]

SILVER (H.) *and* TEAGUE (S.J.) The history of British universities, 1800–1969, excluding Oxford and Cambridge: a bibliography. London: Society for Research into Higher Education, 1970. 264 pp. (016:93) [436]

CRAIGIE (James) A bibliography of Scottish education before 1872. London: Univ. of London Pr., 1970. 251 pp. [437]

CRAIGIE (James) A bibliography of Scottish education 1872–1972. London: Univ. of London Pr., 1974. 279 pp. [438]

CORDEAUX (E.H.) *and* MERRY (D.H.) A bibliography of printed works relating to the University of Oxford. Oxford: Clarendon Pr., 1968. 809 pp. (016:93:37) [439]

c. Germany

ERMAN (W.) *and* HORN (E.) Bibliographie der deutschen Universitäten. Systematisch geordnetes Verzeichnis der bis Ende 1899 gedruckten Bücher und Aufsätze über das deutsche Universitätswesen. Leipzig: Teubner, 1904. 3 vol. [Reprinted 1965 by Georg Olms, Hildesheim] [440]

STARK (E.) Bibliographie zur Universitätsgeschichte. Verzeichnis der im Gebiet der Bundesrepublik Deutschland 1945–1971 veröffentlichten Literatur. Freiburg: Karl Alber, 1974+ (Freiburger Beiträge zur Wissenschafts-geschichte) [441]

XXIV. BIOGRAPHY

1. International
- *a. Bibliographies*
- *b. Indexes*
- *c. Dictionaries*

2. Great Britain
- *a. Bibliographies and Indexes*
- *b. Dictionaries*

3. Other Countries
- *a. Austria*
- *b. Belgium*
- *c. France*
- *d. Germany*
- *e. Italy*
- *f. Netherlands*
- *g. Poland*
- *h. Switzerland*
- *i. U.S.S.R.*
- *j. United States*

1. International

a. Bibliographies

OETTINGER (E.M.) Bibliographie biographique universelle. Dictionnaire des ouvrages relatifs à l'histoire de la vie publique et privée des personnages célèbres de tous les temps et de toutes les nations. Brussels: Stienon, 1854. 2 vol. [442]

RICHES (P.M.) Analytical bibliography of universal collected biography, comprising books published in the English tongue in Great Britain and Ireland, America and the British dominions. London: Library Assn., 1934. 709 pp. [443]

ARNIM (M.) Internationale Personalbibliographie, 1800–1943. 2. Aufl. Leipzig: Hiersemann, 1944–63. 3 vol. [Vol. 3 (1944–59) is by G. Bock and F. Hodes] [444]

SLOCUM (R.B.) Biographical dictionaries and related works. An international bibliography of collective biographies, bio-bibliographies, . . . Detroit, Mich.: Gale Research, 1967. 1056 pp. Suppl. 1-2. 1972–78. (016:92) [445]

b. Indexes

PHILLIPS (L.B.) Dictionary of biographical reference: containing over 100,000 names, together with a classed index of the biographical literature of Europe and America. 3rd ed. London: Low, 1889. 1038 pp. (92(100)) [446]

CHEVALIER (C.U.J.) Répertoire des sources historiques du moyen âge. Bio-bibliographie. Nouvelle éd. Paris: Picard, 1903–1907. 2 vol. [447]

BIOGRAPHY INDEX. A cumulative index to biographical material in books and magazines. New York: Wilson, 1947+ (92(100)) [448]

HYAMSON (A.M.) A dictionary of universal biography of all ages and of all peoples. 2nd ed. London: Routledge and Kegan Paul, 1951. 680 pp. (92(100)) [449]

THE NEW YORK TIMES OBITUARIES INDEX, 1858–1968. New York, 1970. 1136 pp. [450]

INDEX BIO-BIBLIOGRAPHICUS NOTORUM HOMINUM. Edidit Jean Pierre Lobies. Osnabrück: Biblio, 1972+ [An index to articles in some 5,000 biographical dictionaries] (92(100)) [451]

WHO WAS WHO. A cumulative index, 1897–1980.

London: A. & C. Black, 1981. 746 pp. [Index to biographical notices in *Who was who*, vol. 1–7 (1920–81)] [451A]

c. Dictionaries

JÖCHER (C.G.) Allgemeines Gelehrten-Lexicon. Leipzig, 1750–51. 4 vol. [452]

———— ———— Fortsetzung und Ergänzungen von Johann Christophe Adelung [and others]. Leipzig, 1784–1897. 7 vol. (A–ROMULEUS) [453]

MICHAUD (J.F.) Biographie universelle, ancienne et moderne. Nouv. éd. publiée sous la direction de M. Michaud. Paris: Deplaces, 1843–65. 45 vol. [454]

HOEFER (J.C.F.) Nouvelle biographie générale, depuis les temps les plus reculés jusqu'à nos jours, . . . Paris: Didot, 1852–66. 46 vol. (92(100)) [455]

OETTINGER (E.M.) Moniteur des dates, contenant un million de renseignements biographiques, généalogiques et historiques. Leipzig, 1866–82. Supplément. By H. Schramm. 1873. [Reprinted Graz 1964] [455A]

2. Great Britain
a. Bibliographies and Indexes

HART (H.E.R.) *and* JOHNSTON (M.) Bibliography of the registers (printed) of the universities, inns of court, colleges and schools of Great Britain and Ireland. *Bulletin, Institute of Historical Research, University of London*, 9 (1931), 19-30, 65-83, 154-170; 10 (1932), 109-113; 37 (1964), 185-232 [456]

HARLEIAN SOCIETY. Obituary prior to 1800 (as far as relates to England, Scotland and Ireland) compiled by Sir

William Musgrave. Ed. by Sir George J. Armitage. London, 1899–1901. 6 vol. (Publications 44-49) [457]

MATTHEWS (W.) British diaries: an annotated bibliography of British diaries written between 1442 and 1942. Berkeley, Calif.: Univ. of California Pr., 1950. 339 pp. [458]

ROYAL COMMONWEALTH SOCIETY. *Library*. Biography catalogue. By Donald H. Simpson. London, 1961. 511 pp. [459]

HEPWORTH (P.), *Ed.* Select biographical sources. The Library Association manuscripts survey. London: Library Assn., 1971. 154 pp. (930.253) [460]

BATTS (J.S.) British manuscript diaries of the 19th century: an annotated listing. Fontwell: Centaur Pr., 1976. 345 pp. (SML) [461]

b. Dictionaries

ALLIBONE (S.A.) A critical dictionary of English literature, and British and American authors, living and deceased, from the earliest accounts to the latter half of the nineteenth century. Containing over 46,000 articles (authors), with forty indexes of subjects. Philadelphia: Lippincott, 1858. 3 vol. (92(410)) [462]

—— —— Supplement. By John Foster Kirk. Philadelphia: Lippincott, 1891. 2 vol. [463]

DICTIONARY OF NATIONAL BIOGRAPHY. Edited by Leslie Stephen and Sidney Lee. London: Smith, Elder, 1885–1900. 63 vol. (92(410)) [464]

———— First supplement. London, 1901. 3 vol. [465]

———— Index and epitome. London, 1903 [466]

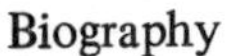

———————— Second supplement. London, 1912. 3 vol. [467]

———————— 1912/21 – 1961/70. London: Oxford Univ. Pr., 1927–81. 6 vol. [Cumulated indexes] (92(410)) [468-470]

———————— The concise dictionary. Part II, 1901–1950. Being an *Epitome* of the twentieth century DNB down to the end of 1950. London: Oxford Univ. Pr., 1961. 528 pp. [471]

———————— Corrections and additions. Cumulated from the Bulletin of the Institute of Historical Research, University of London. Covering the years 1923–1963. Boston, Mass.: G.K. Hall, 1966 [472]

BOASE (F.) Modern English biography, containing many thousand concise memoirs of persons who have died since 1850. Truro: Netherton, 1892–1921. 6 vol. (92(410)) [473]

3. Other Countries

a. Austria

BIOGRAPHISCHES LEXIKON DES KAISERTHUMS ÖSTERREICH. Hrsg. von C. von Wurzbach. Vienna: Zamarski, 1856-1923. 60 vol. [Coverage from 1750] [474]

ÖSTERREICHISCHES BIOGRAPHISCHES LEXIKON, 1815–1950. [Eds.] Leo Santifaller, Eva Obermayer-Marnach. Graz: Böhlaus, 1964+ (93(436)) [475]

b. Belgium

ACADÉMIE ROYALE DES SCIENCES, DES LETTRES ET DES BEAUX ARTS DE BELGIQUE. Biographie nationale. Brussels: Bruyland, 1866–1944. 28 vol. [476]

------ ------ Supplément. Brussels, 1956–71. 9 vol. [477]

KONINKLIJKE VLAAMSE ACADEMIËN VAN BELGIE. Nationaal biografisch woordenboek. Brussels, 1964+ [478]

c. France

DICTIONNAIRE DE BIOGRAPHIE FRANÇAISE. Sous la direction de M. Prévost, puis J. Roman d'Amat et R. Limouzin-Lamothe. Paris: Letouzey & Ané, 1933+ (92(44)) [479]

d. Germany

ALLGEMEINE DEUTSCHE BIOGRAPHIE. Hrsg. durch die Historische Commission bei der Königliche Akademie der Wissenschaften. Leipzig: Duncker & Humblot, 1875–1912. 56 vol. (92(430)) [480]

BIOGRAPHISCHES JAHRBUCH UND DEUTSCHER NEKROLOG 1896–1913. Hrsg. von Anton Bettelheim. Berlin: Georg Reimer, 1897–1917. 18 vol. [481]

NEUE DEUTSCHE BIOGRAPHIE. Hrsg. von der Historischen Kommission bei der Bayerischen Akademie der Wissenschaften. Berlin: Duncker & Humblot, 1953+ (92(430)) [482]

e. Italy

PIZZI (F.) Italica gens. Repertori a stampa di biografia generale italiana. Cremona: Moschetti, 1934. 135 pp. [483]

FERRARI (L.) Onomasticon: repertorio biobibliografico degli scrittori italiani dal 1501 al 1850. Milan: Hoepli, 1947. 708 pp. (92(45)) [484]

COSENZA (M.E.) Biographical and bibliographical dictionary of the Italian humanists and of the world of classical scholarship in Italy, 1300–1800. Boston, Mass.: G.K. Hall, 1962–67. 6 vol. (VAL) [485]

DIZIONARIO BIOGRAFICO DEGLI ITALIANI. Rome: Istituto della Enciclopedia Italiana, 1960+ (92(45)) [486]

f. Netherlands

AA (A.J. van der) Biographisch woordenboek der Nederlanden. Nieuwe uitg. Haarlem: Brederode, 1852–78. 12 vol. (92(492)) [487]

NIEUW NEDERLANDSCH BIOGRAFISCH WOORDENBOEK. Onder red. van P.C. Molhuysen. Leyden: Sythoff, 1911–37. 10 vol. [488]

g. Poland

POLSKA AKADEMJA UMIĘJETNOŚCI (*now* Polska Akademia Nauk). Polski słownik biograficzny. Cracow, 1935+ (92(438)) [489]

h. Switzerland

HISTORISCH-BIOGRAPHISCHES LEXIKON DER SCHWEIZ. Dictionnaire historique et biographique de la Suisse. Sous la direction de M. Godet, H. Turler, V. Attinger. Neuchatel: Adminstration du Dictionnaire, 1921–34. 7 vol., suppl. [490]

i. U.S.S.R.

RÚSSKIĬ BIÓGRAFICESKIĬ SLOVAR'. Moscow, 1896–1918. 25 vol. [491]

j. United States

DICTIONARY OF AMERICAN BIOGRAPHY. Under the auspices of the American Council of Learned Societies. New York: Scribner, 1928–37. 20 vol. (92(73)) [492]

———— Supplements 1-2. New York, 1944–58. 2 vol. [493]

XXV. MANUSCRIPTS AND ARCHIVES

1. *Manuscripts*
2. *Archives*
3. *Bibliographies and Indexes*
   a. *International*
   b. *Great Britain*
4. *Guides to Manuscript Collections and Archives*
   a. *International*
   b. *Great Britain*
   c. *France*
   d. *Germany*
   e. *Hungary*
   f. *Switzerland*
   g. *U.S.S.R.*
   h. *United States*
   i. *The Vatican*
   j. *Yugoslavia*
5. *Catalogues of Manuscripts*
   a. *Great Britain*
   b. *Italy*
   c. *United States and Canada*
   d. *Indian subcontinent*
6. *Palaeography*
   a. *Manuals*
   b. *Dictionaries of Abbreviations*
   [*See also* 92 – 146]

1. *Manuscripts*

LINDSAY (W.M.) An introduction to Latin textual emendation, based on the text of Plautus. London: Macmillan and Co. Ltd., 1896. 131 pp. [494]

HALL (F.W.) A companion to classical texts. Oxford: Clarendon Press, 1913. 363 pp. [A handbook of textual criticism] (Xerox copy of pp. 286-357: the nomenclature of Greek and Latin MSS, at 017/019) [495]

CLARK (A.C.) The descent of manuscripts. Oxford: Clarendon Pr., 1970. 464 pp. [Reprint of 1918 ed.] [496]

SCRIPTORIUM. International review for manuscript studies. Antwerp/Brussels, 1946/47+ [497]

DAIN (A.) Les manuscrits. 3e éd. Paris: Belles Lettres, 1975. 223 pp. [498]

INSTITUT DE RECHERCHE ET D'HISTOIRE DES TEXTES. Bulletin d'information. Paris, 1953+ [499]

DEVRESSE (R.) Introduction à l'étude des manuscrits grecs. Paris: Klincksiek, 1954. 357 pp. [pp. 233-277: sciences] [500]

MARSHALL (R.L.) The historical criticism of documents. London: S.P.C.K., 1920. 62 pp. (Helps for students of history, 28) (SML) [501]

MAAS (Paul) Textual criticism. Tr. by Barbara Flowers. Oxford: Oxford Univ. Pr., 1958. 60 pp. [Summary of the principles for dealing with manuscript texts] [502]

WILLIS (James) Latin textual criticism. Urbana: Univ. of Illinois Pr., 1972. 237 pp. (Illinois studies in language and literature, vol. 61) [503]

WEST (M.L.) Textual criticism and editorial technique applicable to Greek and Latin texts. Stuttgart: Teubner, 1973. 155 pp. [504]

THORPE (James) The use of manuscripts in literary research: problems of access and literary property rights. New York: Modern Language Assn. of America, 1974. 40 pp. [505]

2. Archives

GALBRAITH (V.H.) Studies in the public records. London: Thomas Nelson, 1948. 163 pp. [506]

GALBRAITH (V.H.) An introduction to the use of the public records. 2nd ed. London: Oxford Univ. Pr., 1953. 112 pp. (930.25) [507]

ARCHIVUM. Revue internationale des archives, 1+ Paris, 1951+ [508]

BUSINESS ARCHIVES COUNCIL. Business archives, no. 1+ London, 1956+ [Contains a bibliography and list of business records deposited each year] [509]

FAVIER (J.) Les archives. 3e éd. Paris: Presses Univ. de France, 1975. 124 pp. (Que sais-je? No. 805) [510]

BROOKS (P.C.) Research in archives. The use of unpublished primary sources. Chicago. London: Univ. of Chicago Pr., 1969. 127 pp. (930.25) [511]

IREDALE (David) Enjoying archives. Newton Abbot: David & Charles, 1973. 264 pp. [For beginners] (930.25) [512]

EMMISON (F.G.) Archives and local history. 2nd ed. London: Phillimore, 1974. 112 pp. [First published 1966] (930.25) [513]

3. Bibliographies and indexes

a. International

WEINBERGER (W.) Wegweiser durch die Sammlungen altphilologischer Handschriften. Vienna: Hölder-Pichler-Tempsky, 1930. 136 pp. (*Sitzungsberichte der Österreichische Akademie der Wissenschaften in Wien, philos. hist. Kl.*, 209, Abh. 4) (017/019) [514]

BIBLIOTHÈQUE NATIONALE, PARIS. Catalogue alphabétique des livres imprimés mis à la disposition des lecteurs dans la salle de travail, suivi de la liste des catalogues usuels du Département des Manuscrits. 4e éd. Paris, 1933. 142 pp. [515]

RICHARDSON (E.C.) A list of printed catalogues of manuscript books. (A union world catalogue of manuscript books, vol. 3.) Ed., American Library Assn. New York: Wilson, 1935. 386 pp. (017/019) [516]

BIELER (L.) Les catalogues de manuscrits, premier supplément aux listes de Weinberger et de Richardson. *Scriptorium*, 3 (1949), 303-327 [517]

DJAPARIDZE (D.) Mediaeval Slavic manuscripts: a bibliography of printed catalogues. Cambridge, Mass.: Mediaeval Academy of America, 1957. 134 pp. [518]

VAJDA (G.) Répertoire des catalogues et inventaires de manuscrits arabes. Paris: CNRS, 1949. 49 pp. (Institut de Recherche et d'Histoire des Textes, 2) [519]

RICHARD (Marcel) Répertoire des bibliothèques et des catalogues de manuscrits grecs. 2 ed. Paris: CNRS, 1958. 278 pp. Supplément I (1958–1963). 1964. 77 pp. [520]

UNIVERSITY OF CHICAGO LIBRARY. A provisional list of the catalogues and other inventories of medieval and Renaissance manuscripts, principally Latin and Greek in the University of Chicago libraries. Prepared by Maxime F. Neidinger and Blanche B. Boyer. [Chicago,] 1965. 72 sheets [521]

KRISTELLER (P.O.) Latin manuscript books before 1600: a list of the printed catalogues and unpublished inventories of extant collections. 3rd ed. New York: Fordham Univ. Pr., 1965. 284 pp. (017/019)

Supplements: G. Dogaer, *Scriptorium*, 22 (1968), 84-86; G. Philippart, *Analecta Bollandiana*, 88 (1970), 188-211; C.H. Lohr, *Scriptorium*, 26 (1972), 343-348. [*see also* 92] [522]

PETIT-MENGIN (P.) Répertoire des catalogues de manuscrits en écriture latine antérieurs à 1600 reçus par plusieurs bibliothèques parisiennes. Catalogues parus depuis 1977. Paris: École Normale Supérieure, 1979. 14 sheets. [Typescript] [523A]

JANERT (K.L.) An annotated bibliography of the catalogues of Indian manuscripts. Part I. Wiesbaden: Steiner, 1965. 175 pp. (Verzeichnis der orientalischen Handschriften in Deutschland. Supplementband 1). [524]

HUISMAN (A.J.W.) Les manuscrits arabes dans le monde: une bibliographie des catalogues. Leyden: Brill, 1967. 99 pp. (017/019) [525]

SEZGIN (F.) Bibliotheken und Sammlungen arabischer Handschriften. In: *Geschichte des arabischen Schrifttums* (Leyden, 1967–78), vol. 1, pp. 706-769; vol. 3, pp. 391-410; vol. 5, pp. 446-458; vol. 6, pp. 310-466. [*See* 382] (5(5):93) [525A]

UNIVERSITY OF LONDON LIBRARY. The palaeography collection in the Library: an author and subject catalogue. Boston: G.K. Hall, 1968. 2 vol. [526]

MATEU IBARS (J.) *and* MATEU IBARS (M.D.) Bibliografía paleográfica. Barcelona, 1974. 932 pp. (Universidad de Barcelona, Departmento de Paleografía y Diplomática) [527]

b. Great Britain

HEPWORTH (P.) Archives and manuscripts in libraries. London: Library Assn., 1964. 70 pp. (017/019) [528]

STOREY (Richard) *and* MADDEN (Lionel) Primary guide for Victorian Studies. A guide to the location and use of unpublished materials. London: Phillimore, 1977. 81 pp. (016:941) [529]

HISTORICAL MANUSCRIPTS COMMISSION. A guide to the reports on collections of manuscripts of private families, corporations and institutions in Great Britain and Ireland. London: HMSO, 1914–38. 2 pt. in 3 vol. [530]

HISTORICAL MANUSCRIPTS COMMISSION. Guide to the reports of the Royal Commission on Historical Manuscripts, 1911–1957. London: HMSO, 1966–73. 2 pt. in 4 vol. [531]

HER MAJESTY'S STATIONERY OFFICE. Publications of the Royal Commission on Historical Manuscripts. Government publications sectional list 17. London: HMSO, [Annual] [532]

HER MAJESTY'S STATIONERY OFFICE. British National Archives. Government publications, sectional list 24. London: HMSO, [Annual] [533]

4. Guides to Manuscript Collections and Archives

a. International

SOCIETÉ DES NATIONS. *Institut International de Coopération Intellectuelle.* Guide international des archives. Tome I. Europe. Paris, 1934. 393 pp. [534]

BAUTIER (R.) Bibliographie sélective des guides d'archives. Supplément au *Guide international des archives,* tome 1 (Europe), 1934. *Journal of documentation*, 9 (1953), 1-41. (017/019) [535]

INTERNATIONAL COMMITTEE OF HISTORICAL SCIENCES. *Archives Committee.* Internationaler Archivführer. Bearbeitet von Hans Nabholz und Paul Kläui. Zurich and Leipzig: Rascher, 1936. 110 pp. [536]

INTERNATIONAL COUNCIL ON ARCHIVES. Les grands dépots d'archives du monde: notices sur les archives les plus importantes pour la recherche historique internationale. Paris: Presses Univ. de France, 1969. 374 pp. (*Archivum*, 15 (1965)) (930.25) [537]

MINERVA-HANDBÜCHER. Archive: Archive in deutschsprachigen Raum. 2. Auflage. Berlin: De Gruyter, 1974. 2 vol. (SML) [538]

THOMAS (Daniel H.) *and* CASE (Lynn M.) The new guide to the diplomatic archives of Western Europe. Philadelphia: Univ. of Pennsylvania Pr., 1975. 441 pp. [First published 1959] [539]

INTERNATIONAL COUNCIL ON ARCHIVES. Annuaire internationale des archives. International directory of archives. (A jour en Janvier 1975/ As of January 1975). Paris: Presses Univ. de France, 1975. 480 pp. (*Archivum*, 22/23 (1972/73)) (058:930.25) [540]

WEIL (G.E.) The international directory of manuscripts collections, libraries, private collections, repositories and archives. Paris: Berger-Levrault, 1978+ [Vol. 1, pt. 1: Europe: the manuscript collections. 1978. 301 pp. To be completed in 2 vol. (6 pt.)] (SML) [540A]

b. Great Britain

CAMP (A.J.) Wills and their whereabouts. London: Society of Genealogists, 1963. 137 pp. [A limited 4th ed. (263 pp.) was published privately in 1974] (930.25) [541]

GIBSON (J.S.W.) Wills and where to find them. Chichester, Sussex: Phillimore, 1974. 210 pp. (British Record Society) [542]

ROBERTS (R.A.) The reports of the Historical Manuscripts Commission. London: S.P.C.K., 1920. 91 pp. (Helps for students of history, 22) (SML) [543]

NATIONAL REGISTER OF ARCHIVES. List of accessions to repositories. London: HMSO, [Annual. From 1957] (930.25 TG 72895) [544]

HISTORICAL MANUSCRIPTS COMMISSION. Record repositories in Great Britain. A geographical directory. 6th ed. London, 1979. 35 pp. (930.25) [545]

HISTORICAL MANUSCRIPTS COMMISSION. Secretary's report to the Commissioners. London: HMSO, [Annual] (930.25 TG 8414) [546]

HISTORICAL MANUSCRIPTS COMMISSION. Sources of business history in the National Register of Archives, no. 1-5. London, 1964–72. [No more published] [547]

HISTORICAL MANUSCRIPTS COMMISSION. Sources of business history in the National Register of Archives. First 5-year [1964–9] cumulation. Ed. by R.A. Storey. London, 1971. 149 pp. (930.25 TG 72896) [548]

COOK (Chris) *and* WEEKS (J.) Sources in British political history, 1900–1951. Vol. 5. A guide to the papers of selected writers, intellectuals and publicists. London: Macmillan, 1978. 240 pp. [549]

b (1). Public Record Office

PUBLIC RECORD OFFICE. Guide to the contents of the PRO. London: HMSO, 1963–68. 3 vol. [550]

b (2). British Library

GILSON (J.P.) A student's guide to the manuscripts of the British Museum. London: S.P.C.K., 1920. 48 pp. (Helps for students of history, 31) (SML) [551]

SKEAT (T.C.) The catalogues of the manuscript collections in the British Museum. London: Trustees of the British Museum, 1962. 45 pp. [Originally published in *Journal of documentation*, 7 (1951), 18-60] (017/019) [552]

NICKSON (M.A.E.) The British Library: guide to the catalogues and indexes of the Department of Manuscripts. London: British Library, 1978. 24 pp. (017/019) [553]

b (3). Bodleian Library

CRASTER (H.H.E.) The Western manuscripts of the Bodleian Library. London: S.P.C.K., 1921. 48 pp. (Helps for students of history, 43) (SML) [554]

BODLEIAN LIBRARY, OXFORD. A guide for readers of Western MSS. August 1978. 12 pp. [Reproduced from handwriting] (026:091) [554A]

c. France

HARTMANN (P.C.) Pariser Archive, Bibliotheken und Dokumentationszentren zur Geschichte des 19. und 20. Jahrhunderts: eine Einführung in Benützungspraxis und Bestände für Historiker, Politologen und Journalisten. Munich: Verlag Dokumentation, 1976. 131 pp. (Dokumentation Westeruopa, 1) [555]

CHAULEUR (Andrée) Bibliothèques et archives: comment se documenter? Guide pratique à l'usage des étudiants, des professeurs, des documentalistes et archivistes, des chercheurs . . . 2e éd. Paris: Economica, 1980. 334 pp. [Pp. 1-33: Introduction bibliographique; 33-195: Les bibliothèques et les centres de documentation (39-87: La Bibliothèque Nationale); 197-301: Les archives (206-253: Les Archives Nationales)] (SML) [555A]

DIRECTION DES ARCHIVES, FRANCE. Les Archives Nationales: état général des fonds. Pub. sous la dir. de Jean Favier. Paris, 1978–80. [Vol. 1: L'ancien régime; Vol. 2: 1789–1940; Vol. 3: Marine et outre-mer. Vol. 4–5 *in press*] [555B]

c (1). Bibliothèque Nationale, Paris

BIBLIOTHÈQUE NATIONALE, PARIS. Les catalogues imprimés de la Bibliothèque Nationale. Paris, 1953. 204 pp. [Pp. 5-57: catalogues of MSS] (017/019) [556]

BIBLIOTHÈQUE NATIONALE, PARIS. *Département des Manuscrits.* Les catalogues du Département des manuscrits. Manuscrits occidentaux. Paris, 1974. 102 pp. (017/019) [557]

d. Germany

MOMMSEN (W.A.) Die Nachlässe in den deutschen Archiven (mit Ergänzungen aus anderen Beständen). Bearbeitet im Bundesarchiv in Koblenz. Boppard: Harald Boldt, 1971. 582 pp. (930.253) [558]

DENECKE (L.) Die Nachlässe in Bibliotheken der Bundesrepublik Deutschland. Bearbeitet in der Murhardschen Bibliothek der Stadt Kassel und Landesbibliothek. Boppard: Harald Boldt, 1969. 268 pp. (930.253) [559]

LÜLFING (H.) *and* UNGER (R.) Gelehrten- und Schriftstellernachlässe in den Bibliotheken der Deutschen Demokratischen Republik. Berlin. 1959–68. 2 vol. [560]

HAASE (C.) The records of German history in German and other record offices with short notes on libraries and other collections. Boppard: Harald Boldt, 1975. 194 pp. [561]

DEUTSCHE WIRTSCHAFTSARCHIVE. Nachweis historischer Quellen in Unternehmen, Kämmern und Verbanden der Bundesrepublik Deutschland. Hrsg. im Auftrag der Gesellschaft für Unternehmungsgeschichte e.V. Wiesbaden: Steiner, 1978. [Looseleaf] [562]

e. Hungary

BALAZS (Peter) Guide to the archives of Hungary. Budapest: Archival Board of the Ministry of Culture, 1976. 229 pp. [563]

f. Switzerland

SCHMUTZ-PFISTER (A.M.) Repertorium der handschriftliche Nachlässe in den Bibliotheken und Archiven der Schweiz. Berne: Benteli, 1967. 200 pp. [564]

ARCHIVE, BIBLIOTHEKEN UND DOKUMENTATIONSTELLEN DER SCHWEIZ. 4. Auflage des Führers durch die schweizerische Dokumentation. Berne: Office de la Science et de la Recherche, 1976. 805 pp. [565]

g. U.S.S.R.

GRIMSTED (P.K.) Archives and manuscript repositories in the U.S.S.R.: Moscow and Leningrad. Princeton: Princeton Univ. Pr., 1972. 436 pp. [Includes an account of the growth of archival institutions in the USSR, and an introduction to their practices. The first supplement,

Bibliographical addenda (Zug: Inter Documentation Co., 1976; 203 pp.) contains some 400 annotated items including catalogues of early Slavic MSS. There is also a separately published list of some 600 finding-aids (available in microform) to Soviet archives. For the non-Russian republics, there is Grimsted's *Archives and manuscript repositories in the USSR: Estonia, Latvia, Lithuania, and Belorussia* (Princeton: Princeton Univ. Pr., 1981), 929 pp.] (930.253) [566--568]

h. United States

HAMER (P.) A guide to archives and manuscripts in the United States. New Haven, Conn.: Yale Univ. Pr., 1961. 775 pp. [569]

NATIONAL HISTORICAL PUBLICATIONS AND RECORDS COMMISSION, U.S. Directory of archives and manuscript repositories in the United States. Rev. ed. Washington, 1978. 905 pp. [570]

NATIONAL ARCHIVES AND RECORDS SERVICE, U.S. Guide to the national archives of the United States. Washington, D.C., 1975. 884 pp. [Supersedes: *Guide to the records in the National Archives* (1948)] (930.253) [571]

i. The Vatican

BIGNAMI-ODIER (J.) Guide au Département des manuscrits de la Bibliothèque du Vatican. *Mélanges d'archéologie et d'histoire, École Française de Rome*, 51 (1934), 205-239. (017/019) [572]

FINK (K.A.) Das Vatikanische Archiv: Einführung in die Bestände und ihre Erforschung. 2. Aufl. Rome: W. Regensberg, 1951. 185 pp. [573]

j. Yugoslavia

[*See* 948]

5. Catalogues of Manuscripts

[Catalogues of manuscripts of individual libraries are not listed here. Most academic libraries have good collections of these catalogues. They can easily be traced with the help of: the bibliographies 514-527 above; library directories and guides; the British (Museum's) Library's *General catalogue of printed books* (954-5) the *National Union Catalog* (963). However, some catalogues of scientific manuscripts are listed in chapter V]

a. Great Britain

BERNARD (Edward) Catalogi librorum manuscriptorum Angliae et Hiberniae in unum collecti, cum indice alphabetico [by Humphrey Wanley]. Oxford, 1697. 2 vol. in 1 [574]

KER (N.R.) Medieval manuscripts in British libraries. Oxford: Clarendon Pr., 1969+ [Vol. 1. London. 1969; Vol. 2. Abbotsford–Keele. 1977] (017:091) [575]

HEPWORTH (P.) Select biographical sources: the Library Association manuscripts survey. London: Library Assn., 1971. 154 pp. (932.253) [576]

BATTS (J.S.) British manuscript diaries of the 19th century: an annotated listing. Fontwell: Centaur, 1976. 345 pp. (SML) [577]

b. Italy

KRISTELLER (P.O.) Iter italicum: a finding list of uncatalogued or incompletely catalogued humanistic manuscripts of the Renaissance in Italian and other libraries. London: Warburg Inst., 1965–67. 2 vol. [Vol. 3 *in press*] (017:091) [578] *c. United States and Canada*

LIBRARY OF CONGRESS, WASHINGTON. The National Union Catalog of Manuscript Collections, based on reports from American repositories of manuscripts, 1959/61+ Ann Arbor, Mich.: Edwards, 1962+ (017:091) [579]

RICCI (S. de) Census of medieval and Renaissance manuscripts in the United States and Canada. New York: Wilson, 1935–40. 3 vol. [Kraus reprint 1961] [580]

FAYE (C.U.) *and* BOND (W.H.) Supplement to the census of medieval and Renaissance manuscripts in the United States and Canada. New York: Bibliographical Soc. of America, 1962. 626 pp. [581]

MATTHEWS (William) American diaries in manuscript, 1580–1954; a descriptive bibliography. Athens: Univ. of Georgia Pr., 1974. 176 pp. [582]

d. Indian Subcontinent

AUFRECHT (T.) Catalogus catalogorum: an alphabetical register of Sanskrit works and allied authors. Leipzig: Deutsche Morgenländische Gesellschaft, 1891–1903. 3 vol. [583]

RAGHAVAN (V.) New catalogus catalogorum. An alphabetical register of Sanskrit and allied works and authors. Madras: Univ. of Madras, 1949–74. [8 vol. *In progress*] [584]

6. Palaeography
a. Manuals

CHASSANT (A.A.L.) Paléographie des chartes et des manuscrits du XI au XVII siècles. 8e éd. Augmentée d'une instruction sur les sceaux et leurs légendes et des règles de critique propres à determiner l'âge des chartes et des manuscripts non datés. Paris: Jules Martin, 1885. 159 pp. [585]

THOTYS (E.E.) [How to decipher and study old documents.] How to read old documents. Christchurch: Dolphin Pr., 1972. 143 pp. [Facsimile reprint of 1893 ed.] (930.27) [586]

THOMPSON (E.M.) An introduction to Greek and Latin palaeography. Oxford: Clarendon Pr., 1912. 600 pp. [Reprinted 1965] [587]

HASELDEN (R.B.) Scientific aids for the study of manuscripts. Oxford: Oxford Univ. Pr., 1935. 108 pp. (Supplement to the Bibliographical Society's Transactions, no. 10) [588]

DENHOLM-YOUNG (N.) Handwriting in England and Wales. Cardiff: Univ. of Wales Pr., 1954. 102 pp. [589]

HECTOR (L.C.) The handwriting of English documents. 2nd ed. London: E. Arnold, 1966. 136 pp. [590]

THOMSON (S.H.) Latin bookhands of the later Middle Ages, 1100–1500. Cambridge: Cambridge Univ. Pr., 1970. 132 pp. [591]

SIMPSON (G.G.) Scottish handwriting 1150–1650. Edinburgh: Bratton, 1973. 140 pp. [592]

PETTI (A.G.) English literary hands from Chaucer to Dryden. London: Edward Arnold, 1977. 133 pp. [593]

b. Dictionaries of Abbreviations

MARTIN (C.T.) The record interpreter: a collection of abbreviations, Latin words, and names used in English historical manuscripts and records. 2nd ed. London:

Stevens & Sons, 1910. 464 pp. [Reprinted 1976 by Kohler and Coombes] (413=71) [594]

CAPPELLI (A.) Lexicon abbreviaturarum. Dizionario di abbreviature latine ed italiane. 6 ed. Milan: Hoepli, 1973. 531 pp. (41.18) [595]

PELZER (A.) Abréviations latines médiévales. Supplément au Dizionario di abbreviature latine ed italiane de Adriano Cappelli. 2e ed. Paris: Beatrice-Nauwelaerts, 1966. 86 pp. [596]

CHASSANT (A.A.L.) Dictionnaire des abréviations latines et françaises . . . du moyen âge. 5e éd. Paris: Jules Martin, 1884. 172 pp. [597]

GRUN (P.A.) Schlüssel zu alten und neuen Abkürzungen. Wörterbuch lateinischer und deutscher Abkürzungen des späten Mittelalters und der Neuzeit. Limburg/Lahn: Starke, 1966. 314 pp. [598]

DÜLFER (K.) Gebräuchliche Abkürzungen des 16-20 Jahrhunderts. Marburg, 1966. 40 ff. (Veröffentlichungen der Archivschule Marburg, Nr. 1) [599]

XXVI . CHRONOLOGY

STOCKVIS (A.M.H.J.) Manuel d'histoire, de généalogie, et de chronologie de tous les états du globe. Leyden, 1888–91. 3 vol. [600]

GROTEFEND (H.) Taschenbuch der Zeitrechnung des deutschen Mittelalters und der Neuzeit. 11. Aufl. Hrsg. von Th. Ulrich. Hanover: Hahnsche Buchhandlung, 1971. 224 pp. [First published 1898] [601]

CAPPELLI (A.) Cronologia, cronografia e calendario perpetuo. 2 ed. Milan: Hoepli, 1930. 566 pp. [Reprinted 1960] [602]

CHEYNEY (C.R.) Handbook of dates for students of English history. London: Royal Historical Soc., 1945. 164 pp. [603]

MAYER (Alfred) Annals of European civilization, 1501–1900. London: Cassell, 1949. 458 pp. [604]

FREEMAN-GRENVILLE (G.S.P.) The Muslim and Christian calendars, being tables for the conversion of Muslim and Christian dates from the Hijra to the year AD 2000. 2nd ed. London: Oxford Univ. Pr., 1977. 96 pp. (529) [605]

BOSWORTH (C.E.) The Islamic dynasties: a chronological and genealogical handbook. Edinburgh: Univ. Pr., 1967. 1967. 245 pp. [606]

WISE (L.F.) World rulers from ancient times to the present. London: Ward Lock Educational, 1967. 224 pp. [607]

PASCOE (L.C.), LEE (A.J.) *and* JENKINS (E.S.) The teach yourself encyclopaedia of dates and events. 3rd ed. London: English Universities Pr., 1979. 830 pp. [608]

WILLIAMS Neville) Chronology of the expanding world: 1492 to 1762. London: Barrie and Rockliffe, 1969. 700 pp. [609]

WILLIAMS (Neville) Chronology of the modern world: 1763 to the present time. Rev. ed. London: Barrie and Rockliffe, 1969. 923 pp. [610]

DEL PIAZZO (M.) Manuale di cronologia. Rome: Associazione Nazionale Archivistica Italiana, 1969. 148 pp.[611]

SCHLÖGL (W.) Kalenderrechner Mittelalter und Neuzeit. Munich: Verlag Akademische Buchhandlung, 1971. (Repetitorium der deutschen Geschichte) [612]

STEINBERG (S.H.) Historical tables, 58 B.C. – A.D. 1978. 10th ed. New York: St. Martin's, 1979. 269 pp. [613]

STOREY (R.L.) Chronology of the medieval world: 800 to 1491. General editor: Nevillc Williams. London: Barrie Jenkins, 1973. 705 pp. [614]

FREEMAN-GRENVILLE (G.S.P.) Chronology of world history. A calendar of principal events from 3100 B.C. to A.D. 1973. 2nd ed. London: Collings, 1975. 746 pp. (93) [615]

GRUN (B.) The timetables of history: a chronology of world events based on Werner Stein's *Kulturfahrplan.* London: Thames and Hudson, 1975. 661 pp. (93) [616]

XXVII. SOCIETIES

1. International
2. Great Britain
3. France
4. Germany
5. Italy

1. International

BRITISH MUSEUM. *Department of Printed Books* (*now* British Library) Catalogue of printed books: academies. London, 1885. 1018 col., 100 col. (index). (SML) [617]

ACCADEMIA NAZIONALE DEI LINCEI, ROMA. *Biblioteca.* Elenco bibliografico delle accademie, società, istituti scientifici, direzioni di periodici, ecc., corrispondenti con la R. Accademia dei Lincei e indici delle loro pubblicazioni pervenute all'Accademia, sino a Dicembre 1907. Rome, 1908. 421 pp. [Index of publications was revised in 1952] (05:017) [618]

MINERVA. Internationales Verzeichnis wissenschaftlicher Institutionen. Wissenschaftliche Gesellschaften. 33. Ausgabe (Jahrgang). Hrsg. von Werner Schuder. Berlin: De Gruyter, 1972. 724 pp. (SML) [619]

2. Great Britain

SCIENTIFIC AND LEARNED SOCIETIES OF GREAT BRITAIN. A handbook compiled from official sources. London: Allen & Unwin, 1884+ (06REF) [620]

MULLINS (E.L.C.) A guide to the historical and archaeological publications of societies in England and Wales, 1903–1933; compiled for the Institute of Historical Research. London: Athlone Pr., 1968. 850 pp. (013:061(420)) [621]

HARCUP (S.) Historical, archaeological and kindred societies in the British Isles. A list. Rev. ed. London: University of London, Inst. of Historical Research, 1968. 57 pp. [622]

MACLEOD (R.M.), FRIDAY (J.R.) *and* GREGOR (C.) The corresponding societies of the British Association for the Advancement of Science, 1883–1929. A survey of historical records, archives and publications. London: Mansell, 1975. 147 pp. (06REF) [623]

PERCIVAL (A.C.) The English Association handbook of societies and collections. London: Library Assn. (for the English Assn.), 1977. 139 pp. [624]

3. France

LEFÈVRE-PONTALIS (E.) Bibliographie des sociétés savantes de France. Paris, 1887. 150 pp. (SML) [625]

LASTEYRIE (R. de) *and* VIDIER (A.) Bibliographie générale des travaux historiques et archéologiques publiés par les sociétés savantes de la France depuis les origines jusqu'à 1885 (1900). Paris: Impr. nat., 1888–1918. 6 vol. [626]

BIBLIOGRAPHIE ANNUELLE DES TRAVAUX HISTORIQUES ET ARCHÉOLOGIQUES PUBLIÉS PAR LES SOCIÉTÉS SAVANTES DE LA FRANCE . . . 1901/1902 – 1909/1910. Paris, 1906–14. 3 vol. [627]

GANDILHON (R.) Bibliographie générale des travaux historiques et archéologiques, publiés par les sociétés savantes de la France . . . Période 1910–1940. Paris: Impr. nat., 1944–61. 5 vol. [628]

DENIKER (J.) *and* DESCHARMES (R.) Bibliographie des travaux scientifiques (sciences mathématiques, physiques et naturelles) publiés par les sociétés savantes de la France depuis l'origine jusqu'en 1888, *etc.* Paris: Impr. nat., 1895–1922. 2 vol. [Incomplete] [629]

CARON (P.) *and* JARYC (M.) Répertoire des sociétés françaises de sciences philosophiques, historiques, philologiques et juridiques. Paris: Maison du Livre Français, 1938. 282 pp. [630]

DIRECTION DE BIBLIOTHÈQUES DE FRANCE. *Comité des travaux historiques et scientifiques.* Liste des sociétés savantes et littéraires. 1. Province. Paris, 1958. 58 pp. [631]

4. Germany

MÜLLER (Johannes) Die wissenschaftlichen Vereine und Gesellschaften Deutschlands im neunzehnten Jahrhundert: Bibliographie ihrer Veröffentlichungen seit ihrer Begründung bis auf die Gegenwart. Berlin: Asher, 1883–1917. 2 vol. in 3. [632]

DOMAY (F.) Handbuch der deutschen wissenschaftlichen Akademien und Gesellschaften. Mit einer Bibliographie deutscher Akademie– und Gesellschaftspublikationen. 2. Auflage. Wiesbaden: Steiner, 1977. 1209 pp. (06REF) [633]

5. Italy

MAYLENDER (M.) Storia delle accademie d'Italia. Bologna: Cappelli, 1926–30. 5 vol. [634]

XXVIII. INTERNATIONAL CONGRESSES

UNION DES ASSOCIATIONS INTERNATIONALES. Les congrès internationaux de 1681 à 1899. Liste complète. Brussels, 1960. 76 pp. [635]

DORÉ (R.) Essai d'une bibliographie des congrès internationaux. *Revue des bibliothèques*, 32 (1922), 389-444. [636]

GREGORY (W.) International congresses and conferences, 1840–1937. A union list of their publications available in the libraries of the U.S. and Canada. New York: H.W. Wilson, 1938. 229 pp. (SML) [637]

BRITISH LIBRARY. *Lending Division*. BLL conference index 1964–1973. Boston Spa, 1974. 1220 pp. (013:061.3) [638]

BRITISH LIBRARY. *Lending Division*. Index of conference proceedings received by the BLL. Boston Spa, 1974+ (013:061.3) [639]

XXIX. ATLASES AND GAZETTEERS

1. Atlases

POOLE (R.L.) Historical atlas of modern Europe from the decline of the Roman Empire comprising also maps of parts of Asia, Africa, and the New World connected with European history. Oxford: Clarendon Pr., 1902. 90 maps (and text) [640]

PALMER (R.R.) Rand McNally atlas of world history. New York: Rand McNally, 1957. 216 pp. [641]

PUTZGER (F.W.) Historischer Weltatlas. Jubiläumsausgabe. 85. Auflage. Bielefeld: Velhagen & Klasing, 1963. 146 pp. [642]

TREHARNE (R.F.) *and* FULLARD (H.) Muir's historical atlas: ancient, medieval and modern. New York: Barnes & Noble, 1963. 116 pp. [643]

SHEPHERD (W.R.) Shepherd's historical atlas. 9th ed. New York: Barnes & Noble, 1964. 115 pp. [644]

WESTERMANNS GROSSER ATLAS ZUR WELTGESCHICHTE. Brunswick: Westermann, 1965. 171 pp. [645]

DARBY (H.C.) *and* FULLARD (H.) The new Cambridge modern history. Atlas. Cambridge: Cambridge Univ. Pr., 1970. 319 pp. [646]

KINDER (H.) *and* HILGEMANN (W.) The Penguin atlas of world history. Harmondsworth: Penguin, 1974–78. 2 vol. [Translated from the German] [647]

TIMES BOOKS. Times atlas of world history. Ed., Geoffrey Barraclough. London, 1978. 360 pp. (SML) [648]

ATLAS HISTORIQUE LAROUSSE. Sous la direction de Georges Duby. Paris: Larousse, 1978. 340 pp. (SML)[649]

2. Gazetteers

[See *Horus* (3), p. 77]

BESNIER (M.) Lexique de géographie ancienne. Paris: Klincksieck, 1914. 893 pp. [649A]

CHEVIN (L'Abbé) Dictionnaire latin–français des noms propres de lieux ayant une certaine notoriété principalement au point de vue ecclésiastique et monastique. Bar-Le-Duc: Victor Retaux, 1897. 358 pp. [650]

LIPPINCOTT'S NEW GAZETTEER: a complete pronouncing gazetteer or geographical dictionary of the world. Ed. by Angelo Heilprin and Louis Heilprin. Philadelphia: Lippincott, 1906. 2053 pp. [651]

DESCHAMPS (P.) Dictionnaire de géographie ancienne et moderne; *suivi de* l'Imprimerie hors d'Europe. Paris: Maisonneuve et Larose, 1964. 1591+208 pp. [Originally published in 1870 and 1904 respectively] (655:93) [652]

GRAESSE (J.G.T.) Orbis latinus. Lexikon lateinischer geographischer Namen des Mittelalters und der Neuzeit. 4. Aufl. bearbeitet von Helmut Plechl. Brunswick: Klinkhardt und Biermann, 1972. 3 vol. [First published in 1866] [653]

PEDDIE (R.A.) Place names in imprints. An index to the Latin and other forms used on title pages. London: Grafton, 1932. 69 pp. (413:655.4/5) [654]

COLUMBIA LIPPINCOTT GAZETTEER OF THE WORLD. Ed. by L.E. Seltzer. New York: Columbia Univ. Pr., 1952. 2148 pp. Suppl. 1961. 23 pp. (Gazetteer (100)) [655]

XXX. DICTIONARIES (Historical)

STARNES (D.T.) Renaissance dictionaries, English–Latin and Latin–English. Austin: Univ. of Texas Press, 1954. 427 pp. [656]

ZAUNMÜLLER (W.) Bibliographisches Handbuch der Sprachwörterbücher. Ein internationales Verzeichnis von 5600 Wörterbüchern der Jahre 1460–1958 für mehr als 500 Sprachen und Dialekte. Stuttgart: Hiersemann, 1958. 496 col. [657]

TONELLI (G.) A short-title list of subject dictionaries of the sixteenth, seventeenth and eighteenth centuries as aids to the history of ideas. London: The Warburg Institute, 1971. 64 pp. (5(02):93) [658]

DU CANGE (C. Du Fresne) Glossarium mediae et infimae latinitatis. Paris, 1840–50. 7 vol. (413=71) [659]

MAIGNE D'ARNIS (W.H.) Lexicon manuale ad scriptores mediae et infimae latinitatis . . . ou, Recueil de mots de la basse latinité. Publié par M. l'Abbé Migne. Paris, 1890. 2335 col. [660]

NIERMEYER (J.F.) Mediae latinitatis lexicon minus. Lexique latin médiéval – français/anglais. A medieval Latin – French/English dictionary. (Abbreviationes et index fontium). Leyden: Brill, 1976. 2 vols. (413=71) [661]

LATHAM (R.E.) Revised medieval Latin word-list from British and Irish sources. London: Oxford Univ. Pr. (for the British Academy), 1965. 524 pp. (413=71) [662]

DOURSTHER (H.) Dictionnaire universel des poids et mesures anciens et modernes, contenant des tables des monnaies de tous les pays. Amsterdam: Meridian Publishing Co., (1965). 604 pp. [Reprint of the 1840 edition] (531.7:93) [663]

ZUPKO (R.E.) A dictionary of English weights and measures: from Anglo-Saxon times to the nineteenth century. Madison: Univ. of Wisconsin Pr., 1968. 224 pp. (531.7:93) [664]

STEARN (W.T.) Botanical Latin: history, grammar, syntax, terminology, and vocabulary. 2nd ed. rev. Newton Abbot: David and Charles, 1973. 566 pp. (807.1) [665]

PART III

General Reference

[666 – 1034]

XXXI. GUIDES TO REFERENCE BOOKS

1. *Bibliography*

MALCLÈS (L.N.) La bibliographie. 4e éd. Paris: Presses Univ. de France, 1977. 126 pp. (Que sais-je? No. 708) [Good survey of systematic bibliography, from Symphorien Champier and Conrad Gesner to Poggendorff and Besterman. The author, Librarian of the Sorbonne for many years, was a distinguished teacher of bibliography. *See also* 680 and 686] [666]

COLLISON (R.L.W.) Bibliographies, subject and national. A guide to their contents, arrangement and use. 3rd ed. London: Crosby Lockwood, 1968. 203 pp. (011/016) [667]

2. *Bibliographies of Bibliographies*

PETZHOLDT (J.) Bibliotheca bibliographica. Kritisches Verzeichnis der das Gesamtgebiet der Bibliographie betreffenden Litteratur des In- und Auslandes in systematischer Ordnung. Leipzig, 1866. 939 pp. [Reprinted Nieuwkoop in 1972] (011/016) [667A]

BIBLIOGRAPHIC INDEX. A cumulative bibliography of bibliographies. New York. Wilson, 1938+ [Quarterly. Annual cumulation] (011/016) [668]

BOHATTA (H.) *and* HODES (F.) Internationale Bibliographie der Bibliographien: ein Nachschlagwerk. Vol. 1. Frankfurt-on-Main: Klostermann, 1950. 652 pp. [General, national and subject bibliographies] [669]

TAYLOR (Archer) A history of bibliographies of bibliographies. New Brunswick: Scarecrow, 1055. 147 pp [670]

BIBLIOGRAPHIE DER VERSTECKTEN BIBLIOGRAPHIEN: aus deutschsprachigen Büchern und Zeitschriften der Jahre 1930–1953. Leipzig: Deutsche Bücherei, 1956. 371 pp. [671]

BIBLIOGRAPHIE DER DEUTSCHEN BIBLIOGRAPHIEN. Jahresverzeichnis der selbstandig erschienenen und der in deutschsprachigen Büchern und Zeitschriften enthaltenen versteckten Bibliographien. Jg. 1 (1954)+ Leipzig: Deutsche Bücherei, 1957+ [672]

BESTERMAN (T.) A world bibliography of bibliographies and of bibliographical catalogues. 4th ed. Lausanne: Societas Bibliographica, 1965–1966. 5 vol. [Classified bibliography of some 117,000 vol. of bibliographies under 16,000 headings. Review: *Bull. bibliothèques de France*, 1956, pp. 835-836] (011/016) [673] *

TOOMEY (A.F.) A world bibliography of bibliographies, 1964–1974. A list of works represented by Library of Congress printed catalog cards. A decennial supplement to Theodore Besterman. Totowa, N.J.: Rowman and Littlefield, 1977. 2 vol. (011/016) [674]

REFERENCE SERVICES REVIEW. Ann Arbor, Mich.: Pierian Pr., 1973+ [Quarterly] [675]

MARK (Linda), *Ed.* Reference sources. Ann Arbor, Mich.: Pierian Pr., 1977+ [Annual] [676]

3. Guides to Reference Books

STEIN (H.) Manuel de bibliographie générale (Bibliotheca bibliographica nova). Paris: Picard, 1897. 895 pp. (011/016) [677]

SCHNEIDER (G.) Handbuch der Bibliographie. 4. Aufl. Leipzig: Hiersemann, 1930. 674 pp. (011/016) [678]

CALOT (F.) *and* THOMAS (G.) Guide pratique de bibliographie. 2e éd. Paris: Delagrave, 1950. 278 pp. [679]

MALCLÈS (L.N.) Les sources du travail bibliographique. Geneva: Droz, 1950-58. 3 vol. in 4.
[Not to be dismissed as the French counterpart of Walford (682) or Winchell/ Sheehy (687). Written in the form of a text-book (treating bibliography as an independent discipline), it aims at guiding the user "au coeur des questions". About 20,000 items. Vol. 1 deals with general bibliographies; vol. 2 (in 2 pt.) with languages and literature, the arts, the social sciences, history, geography, religion and philosophy; vol. 3 with the pure and applied sciences (some chapters by specialists). Gives not only bibliographies and other reference works, but also monographs, collections of sources, and periodicals. Review: *Journal of documentation*, 7 (1951), 188-191; 9 (1953), 63-69; 15 (1959), 156-159] (011/016) [680] *

ZISCHKA (G.A.) Index lexicorum: Bibliographie der lexikalischen Nachschlagwerke. Vienna: Brüder Hollinek, 1959. 290 pp. [7,000 encyclopedias and dictionaries. International in scope; arranged in 21 sections (subdivided). No language dictionaries. Index of names and subject headings. Introduction (44 pp.) contains a history of encyclopedias. Described in Ferguson (12)] (011/016) [681] *

WALFORD (A.J.) Guide to reference material. 3rd ed. London: Library Assn., 1973–77. 3 vol. Vol. 1: Science and technology. Vol. 2: Social and historical sciences. Vol. 3: Generalities, languages, the arts and literature.
[Some 15,000 entries, classified and annotated. Emphasis on British works. Combined subject index to all three volumes. *See* 148 for 4th ed., Vol. 1. Review of 2nd ed.: *Journal of documentation*, 23 (1967), 82-84.] (011/016) [682] *

WALFORD (A.J.) Walford's concise guide to reference material. London: Library Assn., 1981. 434 pp. [A shortened version of the three-volume guide. Basic items updated and more recent material added. Some 2,600 main entries. English-language and British emphasis more pronounced] [682A]

TOTOK (W.), WEIMANN (K.H.) *and* WEITZEL (R.) Handbuch der bibliographischen Nachschlagwerke. 4. Aufl. Frankfurt-on-Main: Klostermann, 1972. 367 pp. [Review of 2nd ed.: *Bull. bibliothèques de France*, 1959, pp. 393-405] (011/016) [683]

CHEYNEY (F.N.) Fundamental reference sources. Chicago: American Library Assn., 1971. 328 pp. [684]

WYNAR (B.S.) Reference books in paperback: an annotated guide. Littleton, Colo.: Libraries Unlimited, 1972. 199 pp. [685]

MALCLÈS (L.N.) Manuel de bibliographie. 3e éd. revue et mise à jour par Andrée Lhéritier. Paris: Presses Univ. de France, 1976. 398 pp. [Classic of bibliography written for the use of university students (in all disciplines) and student-librarians. Excellent introduction to bibliographical tools. Review of 1st ed.: *Journal of documentation*, 20 (1964), 91-93] (011/016) [686]

AMERICAN LIBRARY ASSOCIATION. Guide to reference books. 9th ed. by E.P. Sheehy. Chicago, 1976. 1015 pp. First suppl. 1980. 350 pp.
[Annotated, classified bibliography of some 8,000 reference books, with brief introductory notes to each section. Updated by half-yearly surveys in *College and research libraries*. Eighth ed. (1967) by Constance M. Winchell, with three supplements (1968–72); review in: *Bull. bibliothèques de France*, 1968, pp. 369-370] (011/016) [687] *

HIGGENS (Gavin), *Ed.* Printed reference material. London: Library Assn., 1980. 520 pp. [Critical survey of reference material. Subjects include: dictionaries; encyclopedias; biography; directories; newspapers and almanacs; periodicals; reports, theses; atlases, gazeteers; government publications; local history; bibliography; on-line information retrieval systems] (011/016) [687A]

MUEHSAM (Gerd) Guide to basic information sources in the visual arts. Santa Barbara, Calif.: Jeffrey Norton, 1978. 266 pp. (084) [688]

4. Catalogues of Bibliographical Works

PAYNE (L.M.) *and* HARRIES (J.M.) Reference books and bibliographies: a union catalogue. London: Assn. of Assistant Librarians, 1957. 92 pp. [Still useful as it gives locations (of standard reference works) in London libraries. Written for the use of student-librarians] (011/016) [689]

HARVARD UNIVERSITY LIBRARY. Widener Library shelflist, 7. Bibliography and bibliography periodicals. Cambridge, 1966. 1066 pp. [690]

HARVARD UNIVERSITY LIBRARY. Widener Library shelflist, 33. Reference collections shelved in the Reading Room and Acquisitions Department. Cambridge, 1970. 130 pp. [691]

LIBRARY OF CONGRESS. The Library of Congress main Reading Room reference collection subject catalog. Compiled by Katherine Ann Gardner. Washington: 1975. 638 pp. [692]

XXXII. EARLY PRINTED BOOKS

1. *Bibliographies of Bibliographies*
2. *Union Catalogues*
3. *Library Catalogues*
4. *Bibliographies*

1. *Bibliographies of Bibliographies*

CHILDS (J.B.) Sixteenth century books. A bibliography of literature describing books published between 1501 and 1601. *Papers, Bibliographical Society of America*, 17 (1923), 73-152. [693]

JAYNE (Sears) Library catalogues of the English Renaissance. Berkeley: Univ. of California Pr., 1956. 225 pp. [694]

BESTERMAN (T.) Early printed books to the end of the sixteenth century: a bibliography of bibliographies. 2nd ed. Geneva: Societas Bibliographica, 1961. 344 pp. [695]

WAGNER (F.G.) Bibliotheca bibliographica librorum sedicimi saeculi. Bibliographisches Repertorium fur die Drucke des 16. Jhs. Aureliae Aquensis (Baden-Baden): Koerner, 1960. 83 pp. (Bibliotheca bibliographica Aureliana, 3) [696]

BERKOWITZ (D.S.) Bibliotheca bibliographica incunabula; a manual of bibliographical guides to inventories of printing, of holdings, and of reference aids. Waltham, Mass., 1967. 336 pp. [697]

READ (E. Anne) A checklist of books, catalogues and periodical articles relating to the Cathedral libraries of England. Oxford: Oxford Bibliographical Society, 1970. 59 pp. (Occasional publications, 6). [Suppl. in: *Library history*, 4 (1978), 141-163] [698-699]

BRITISH LIBRARY. *Reference Division.* Guide to the union catalogues of books printed before 1801 and to other tools for locating antiquarian books in Western languages. Provisional draft. 1977. [Typescript. For consultation in the North Library Reading Room in the British Library. Includes: Directory of British and Irish libraries] [700]

MUNBY (A.N.L.) *and* CORAL (L.) British book sale catalogues, 1676–1800. A union list. London: Mansell, 1977. 146 pp. [Based on: *List of catalogues of English book sales 1676–1900 now in the British Museum.* London: British Museum, 1915. 523 pp.] (016:017.3) [701]

2. Union Catalogues

GOFF (F.R.) Incunabula in American libraries; a third census of fifteenth-century books recorded in North American collections. New York: Bibliographical Society of America, 1964. 798 pp. Suppl. 1972. 104 pp. [The 1964 ed. was reprinted by Kraus in 1973 from the annotated copy maintained by F.R. Goff] [701A]

GESAMTKATALOG DER WIEGENDRUCKE. Hrsg. von der Kommission fur den Gesamtkatalog. 2. Aufl. Stuttgart: Hiersemann, 1968–78. [Bd. 1-8 (Abano–Flühe). *In progress*. For description *see* Sheehy (687)] (017:093)[702]

HAIN (L.F.T.) Repertorium bibliographicum, in quo libri omnes ab arte typographica inventa usque ad annum MD typis expressi ordine alphabetico vel simpliciter enumerantur vel adcuratius recensentur. Milan: Görlich Editore, 1966. 2 vol. in 4. [Reprint of the 1826–38 edition] (017:093) [703]

COPINGER (W.A.) Supplement to Hain's Repertorium Bibliographicum, or collections towards a new edition of that work. In two parts . . . with . . . index by Konrad Burger. Berlin: Josef Altmann, 1926. 2 vol. [Reproduction of the 1895–1902 edition] (017:093) [704]

REICHLING (D.) Appendices ad Hainii-Copingeri repertorium bibliographicum. Additiones et emendationes. Milan: Gorlich Editore, 1953. 7 pt. in 2 vol. [Reprint of the 1905–14 edition] (017:093] [705]

INDEX AURELIENSIS. Catalogus librorum sedecimo saeculo impressorum. Aureliae Aquensis (Baden-Baden): Heitz, 1965–76. [6 vol. *In progress*] (Bibliotheca bibliographica Aureliana, 7+) [706]

VALENZIANI (E.), CERULLI (E.) *and* VENEZIANI (P.) Indice generale degli incunaboli delle biblioteche d'Italia. A cura del Centro Nazionale d'Informazioni Bibliografiche. Rome: Istituto Poligrafico dello Stato, 1942–72. 5 vol. [707]

POLLARD (A.) *and* REDGRAVE (G.R.) A short-title catalogue of books printed in England, Scotland, and Ireland and of English books, printed abroad, 1475–1640. 4th imp. London: The Bibliographical Society, 1950. 609 pp. [Originally issued in 1926. Vol. 2 of 2nd ed. published 1975] (017:093) [708]

WING (D.G.) Short-title catalogue of books printed in England, Scotland, Ireland, Wales, and British America and of English books printed in other countries, 1641–1700. New York: printed for the Index Society by Columbia Univ. Pr., 1945–51. 3 vol. [Vol. 2 of 2nd ed. published 1976 by the Bibliographical Society, London] (017:093) [709]

ADAMS (H.M.) Catalogue of books printed on the continent of Europe, 1501–1600, in Cambridge libraries. Cambridge: Univ. Pr., 1967. 2 vol. (017:093) [711]

RHODES (D.E.) A catalogue of incunabula in all the libraries of Oxford University outside the Bodleian. Oxford: Clarendon Pr. [*In press*] [711A]

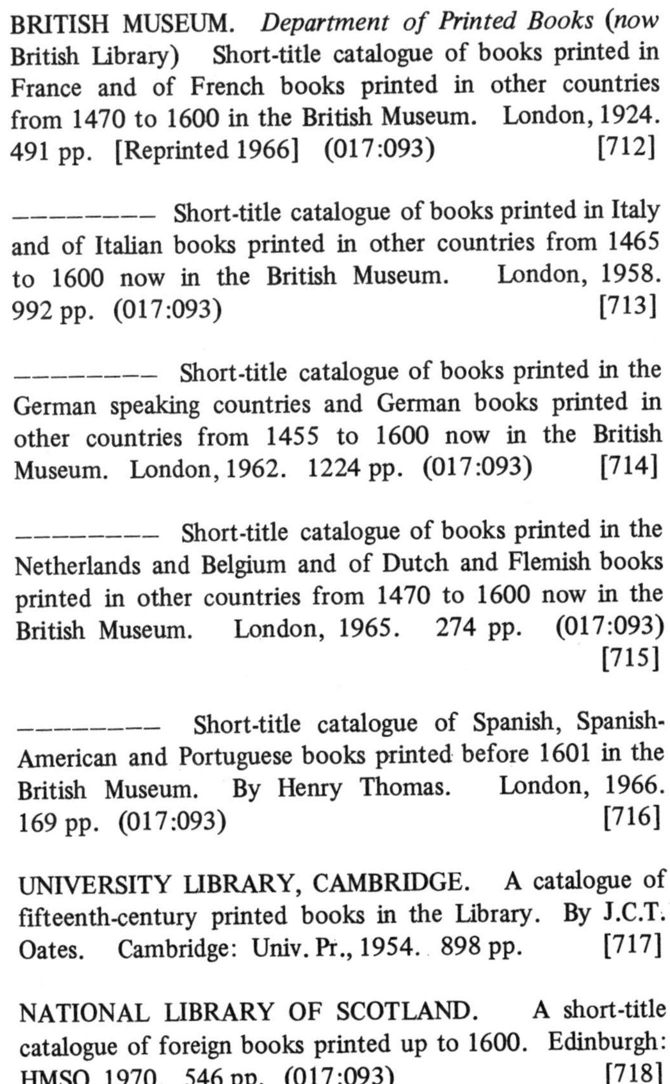

3. Library Catalogues

BRITISH MUSEUM. *Department of Printed Books* (*now* British Library) Short-title catalogue of books printed in France and of French books printed in other countries from 1470 to 1600 in the British Museum. London, 1924. 491 pp. [Reprinted 1966] (017:093) [712]

————— Short-title catalogue of books printed in Italy and of Italian books printed in other countries from 1465 to 1600 now in the British Museum. London, 1958. 992 pp. (017:093) [713]

————— Short-title catalogue of books printed in the German speaking countries and German books printed in other countries from 1455 to 1600 now in the British Museum. London, 1962. 1224 pp. (017:093) [714]

————— Short-title catalogue of books printed in the Netherlands and Belgium and of Dutch and Flemish books printed in other countries from 1470 to 1600 now in the British Museum. London, 1965. 274 pp. (017:093) [715]

————— Short-title catalogue of Spanish, Spanish-American and Portuguese books printed before 1601 in the British Museum. By Henry Thomas. London, 1966. 169 pp. (017:093) [716]

UNIVERSITY LIBRARY, CAMBRIDGE. A catalogue of fifteenth-century printed books in the Library. By J.C.T. Oates. Cambridge: Univ. Pr., 1954. 898 pp. [717]

NATIONAL LIBRARY OF SCOTLAND. A short-title catalogue of foreign books printed up to 1600. Edinburgh: HMSO, 1970. 546 pp. (017:093) [718]

DAY (J.C.) A short title catalogue of books (English and Continental) printed before 1701 in the Thomlinson collection, Newcastle upon Tyne Central Library. (Thesis submitted for Fellowship of the Library Association, 1970). [Some 6,000 titles, including a good selection of works on medicine, alchemy and mathematics] Ann Arbor, Mich.: Univ. Microfilms, 1970. 462 + 92 sheets. [719]

4. Bibliographies

STILLWELL (M.B.) Incunabula and americana, 1450–1800. New York: Columbia Univ. Pr., 1931. 483 pp. [720]

BIBLIOTHECA BELGICA. Bibliographie générale des Pays-Bas. Fondée par Ferdinand van der Haeghen. Ed., M.T. Lenger. Brussels: Culture et Civilisation, 1964–75. 7 vol. [Reprint of ed. begun in 1880] (017:093) [721]

XXXIII. NATIONAL BIBLIOGRAPHIES

1. Bibliographies of Bibliographies
2. National Bibliographies
a. General
b. English Language
c. French Language
d. German Language

1. Bibliographies of Bibliographies

PINTO (Olga) Le bibliografie nazionali. 2 ed. Florence: Olschki, 1951. 95 pp. [Suppl. in: *La Bibliofilia*, 1957, pp. 35-54, and 1963, pp. 57-80.] (015) [722-723]

CONOVER (H.F.) Current national bibliographies. Washington: Library of Congress, 1955. 132 pp. (015) [724]

COURTNEY (W.B.) A register of national bibliography; with a selection of the chief bibliographical books and articles printed in other countries. London: Constable, 1905–12. 3 vol. [725]

SCHNEIDER (G.) Handbuch der Bibliographie. 4. Aufl. Leipzig: Hiersemann, 1930. Pp. 159-368. (011/016) [726]

2. National Bibliographies

[Few *current* national bibliographies are given here. They are listed in full in Walford (682), Sheehy (687) and Malclès (686). A good survey of national bibliographies can be found in Malclès (680), vol. 1, pp. 112-212. *See also* 722-726 above]

a. General

WATT (R.) Bibliotheca britannica; or, A general index to British and foreign literature. Edinburgh: Constable, 1824. 4 vol. (011) [727]

b. English Language

ENGLISH CATALOGUE OF BOOKS ISSUED IN GREAT BRITAIN AND IRELAND, 1801+ London: Publisher's Circular, 1864+ [Irregular] (015(410)) [728]

LOWNDES (W.T.) Bibliographer's manual of English literature. New ed. London: Bell, 1858–64. 6 vol. in 11. (015(410)) [729]

BRITISH BOOKS IN PRINT 1981. The reference catalogue of current literature. London: Whitaker, 1981. 2 vol. (015(410)) [Annual] [730]

BOOKS IN PRINT 1980–81. New York: Bowker, 1980. 4 vol. [Annual] [731]

SUBJECT GUIDE TO BOOKS IN PRINT 1980–81. New York: Bowker, 1980. 2 vol. [Annual] [732]

INTERNATIONAL BOOKS IN PRINT 1979. English-language titles published outside the U.S.A. and the United Kingdom. Munich: K.G. Saur, 1979. 2 vol. [732A]

c. French Language

QUÉRARD (J.M.) La France littéraire ou Dictionnaire bibliographique des savants, historiens et gens de lettres de la France ainsi que des littérateurs étrangers qui ont écrit en français plus particulièrement pendant les XVIIIe et XIXe siècles. Paris: Didot, 1827–64, 12 vol. (015(44)) [733]

QUÉRARD (J.M.) La littérature française contemporaine. Paris: Daguin, 1840–57. 6 vol. (015(44)) [734]

LORENZ (O.) Catalogue générale de la librarie française. Paris, 1867–1945. 34 vol. [Covers period 1840–1925] (015(44)) [735]

CERCLE DE LA LIBRAIRIE. Les livres disponibles 80/81. French books in print. Auteurs, titres, sujets. Paris, 1980. 3 vol. [Annual] [736]

d. German Language

HEINSIUS (W.) Allgemeines Bücherlexikon oder vollständiges alphabetisches Verzeichnis aller von 1700 bis Ende 1892 erschienenen Bücher. Leipzig, 1812–94. 19 vol. [737]

KAYSER (C.G.) Vollständiges Bücherlexikon, 1750–1910. Leipzig, 1834–1911. 36 vol. (015(430)) [738]

VERZEICHNIS LIEFERBARER BÜCHER. German books in print, 1980/81. Frankfurt-on-Main: Buchhändlervereinigung, 1980. 4 vol. [Annual] (015(430)) [739]

XXXIV. OFFICIAL PUBLICATIONS

1. General
2. Great Britain
3. United States

1. General

MEYRIAT (J.) Étude des bibliographies courantes des publications officielles nationales: guide sommaire et inventaire. A study of current national official publications: short guide and inventory. Paris: UNESCO, 1958. 260 pp. (Manuels bibliographiques de l'UNESCO, 7) [740]

PARSONS (K.A.C.) *and* VICKERY (R.C.G.) Outline guide to official publications in Cambridge University Library (excluding scientific material). Enlarged and revised by W.A. Noblett. Cambridge: Univ. Library, 1976. 164 pp. (Librarianship series, 3) (017:087.7) [741]

PALIC (V.M.) Government publications: a guide to bibliographic tools. 4th ed. Washington, D.C.: Library of Congress, 1975. 441 pp. [742]

2. Great Britain

OLLÉ (J.G.) An introduction to British government publications. 2nd ed. London: Association of Assistant Librarians, 1973. 175 pp. (015(410)) [743]

PEMBERTON (J.E.) British official publications. 2nd rev. ed. Oxford: Pergamon, 1973. 328 pp. [744]

JOHANSSON (E.) Current British government publishing. London: Assn. of Assistant Librarians, S.E. Division, 1978. 64 pp. (655.1) [745]

RODGERS (Frank) A guide to British government publications. New York: H.W. Wilson, 1980. 750 pp. [Reviewed in *State librarian*, 29 (1981), 28]. [745A]

BRITISH LIBRARY. *Reference Division.* Checklist of British official serial publications. 10th ed. By Eve Johansson and Nicola Brown. London, 1979. 92 pp. (05:017) [746]

RICHARD (Stephen) British government publications: an index to chairmen (of Committees and Commissions of Inquiry) and authors, 1800–1899, 1900–1940, and 1941–1978. London: Library Assn., 1974–82. 3 vol. [Vol. 3 (for 1941–1978) is a cumulation and revision of two separate indexes published by A.M. Morgan and L.R. Stephen in 1969 and 1976] [747–9]

BOND (M.F.) The records of Parliament: a guide for genealogists and local historians. Canterbury: Phillimore & Co., 1964. 54 pp. [750]

BOND (M.F.) Guide to the records of Parliament. London: HMSO, 1971. 352 pp. (930.25) [751]

FORD (P.) *and* FORD (G.) A guide to parliamentary papers. What they are, how to find them, how to use them. 3rd ed. Shannon: Irish Univ. Pr., 1972. 79 pp. (SML) [752]

HIS MAJESTY'S STATIONERY OFFICE. Index to local and personal acts, consisting of classified lists of the local and personal and private acts and special orders and special procedure orders 1801–1947. London, 1949. 1140 pp. (013:015(410)) [753]

BLACKMORE (R.M.) Cumulative index to the annual catalogues of Her Majesty's Stationery Office publications, 1922–1972. Washington, D.C.: Carrollton Pr., 1976. 2 vol. [754]

3. United States

MOREHEAD (Joe) Introduction to United States public documents. 2nd ed. Littleton, Colo.: Libraries Unlimited, 1978. 377 pp. (015(73)) [755]

JACKSON (Ellen) Subject guide to major United States government publications. Chicago: American Library Assn., 1968. 175 pp. [756]

KANELY (E. A.) Cumulative subject guide to U.S. government bibliographies 1924–1973. Arlington, Va.: Carrollton Pr., 1976. 7 vol. [757]

BUCHANAN (W.W.) *and* KANELY (E.A.) Cumulative subject index to the monthly catalogue of U.S. government publications, 1900–1971. Washington, D.C.: Carrollton Pr., 1973–75. 15 vol. [758]

DOWNEY (J.A.) U.S. Federal official publications. New ed. Oxford: Pergamon, 1978. 352 pp. [758A]

XXXV. THESES AND DISSERTATIONS

1. *Bibliographies of Bibliographies*
2. *Libraries Holding Foreign Theses*
3. *Retrospective Indexes to Theses*
   a. *Great Britain and Ireland*
   b. *United States and Canada*
   c. *France*
   d. *Germany*
4. *Current Indexes to Theses*

1. Bibliographies of Bibliographies

PALFREY (R.) *and* COLEMAN (H.E.) Guide to bibliographies of theses, United States and Canada. Chicago: American Library Assn., 1940. 54 pp. [759]

BLACK (D.M.) Guide to lists of master's theses. Chicago: American Library Assn., 1965. 144 pp. [760]

REYNOLDS (M.M.) A guide to theses and dissertations; an annotated international bibliography of bibliographies. Detroit: Gale, 1975. 599 pp. (013:378) [761]

2. Libraries Holding Foreign Theses

JOHNSON (R.S.) Foreign theses in British libraries. Cardiff: SCONUL, 1971. 27 pp. (017:378) [762]

BODLEIAN LIBRARY. Catalogus dissertationum academicarum quibus nuper aucta est Bibliotheca Bodleiana 1832. Oxford, 1834. 448 pp., index. [763]

3. Retrospective Indexes to Theses

a. Great Britain and Ireland

BILBOUL (R.R.) Retrospective index to theses of Great

Britain and Ireland, 1716–1950. Oxford: Clio Pr., 1975–76. 5 vol. (013:378) [764]

JACOBS (P.M.) History theses, 1901–70: historical research for higher degrees in the universities of the United Kingdom. London: Univ. of London Inst. of Historical Research, 1976. 456 pp. (013:378) [765]

BELL (S.P.) Dissertations on British history, 1815–1914: an index to British and American theses. Metuchen, N.J.: Scarecrow Pr., 1974. 232 pp. (92:62) [766]

MORGAN (Raine) Dissertations on British agrarian history: a select list of theses awarded higher degrees in British and foreign universities between 1876 and 1978. Reading: Univ. of Reading Inst. of Agric. Hist., 1981. 170 pp. [766A]

b. United States and Canada

MACKWORTH (M.L.) Dissertations in physics: an indexed bibliography of all doctoral theses accepted by American Universities, 1861–1959. Stanford, Calif.: Stanford Univ. Pr., 1961. 803 pp. (013:378) [767]

KUEHL (W.F.) Dissertations in history. An index to dissertations completed in History Departments of United States and Canadian universities 1873–1960 [and] 1961–June 1970. Lexington: Univ. of Kentucky Pr., 1965–72. 2 vol. [768]

COMPREHENSIVE DISSERTATION INDEX 1861–1972. Ann Arbor, Mich.: Univ. Microfilms, 1973. 37 vol. [769]

c. France

MAIRE (Albert) Catalogue des thèses de sciences soutenues en France de 1810 à 1890 inclusivement. Paris: Welter, 1892. 224 pp. (013:378) [770]

LAVAUD (Suzanne) Catalogue des thèses de doctorat ès sciences naturelles soutenues à Paris de 1891 à 1954. Paris: Person, 1955. 257 pp. (Bibliothèque de la Faculté de Pharmacie de Paris) [771]

d. Germany

MUNDT (H.) Bio-bibliographisches Verzeichnis von Universitäts- u. Hochschuldrucken: (Dissertationen) vom Ausgang des 16. bis Ende des 19. Jahrhunderts. Leipzig: Carlsohn, 1936–42. 2 vol. [*Incomplete.* Reprinted 1965 by Johnson] (013:378) [772]

4. Current Indexes to Theses

DISSERTATION ABSTRACTS, Vol. 1+. Ann Arbor, Mich.: Univ. Microfilms, 1938+ [Title changed in 1969 to *Dissertations abstracts international.* Monthly] (013:378) [773]

ASLIB. Index to theses accepted for higher degrees in the universities of Great Britain and Ireland, 1 (1950/51)+ London, 1953+ [Annual] (013:378) [774]

UNIVERSITY OF LONDON. *Institute of Historical Research.* Historical research for university degrees in the United Kingdom, 1930/31+ London, 1931+ [From 1932/ to 1965, issued as suppl. to the *Bulletin of the Institute. Annual]* (013:378) [775]

BRITISH SOCIETY FOR THE HISTORY OF SCIENCE. A list of theses in the history of science in British universities in progress or recently completed. Session 72/73+ London, 1973+ [Annual] (013:378) [776]

LIST OF DOCTORAL DISSERTATIONS IN HISTORY now in progress or completed at universities in the United States, 1909+ Washington, New York, 1909+ [Details in Sheehy (687). Publisher varies] [777]

XXXVI. ENCYCLOPEDIAS

1. Bibliographies
2. English [language]
3. Dutch
4. French
5. German
6. Italian
7. Russian
8. Portuguese
9. Spanish

1. Bibliographies

JOHN CRERAR LIBRARY, CHICAGO. A list of cyclopedias and dictionaries, with a list of directories, August 1904. Chicago, 1904. 272 pp. [778]

ZISCHKA (G.A.) Index lexicorum: Bibliographie der lexikalischen Nachschlagwerke. Vienna: Hollinek, 1959. 290 pp. [*See* 681] (011/016) [779]

BRITISH MUSEUM. *Department of Printed Books.* Encyclopaedias. In: General catalogue of printed books, vol. 61 (1961), col. 592-670. (017(410)) [780]

ENCYCLOPÉDIES ET CIVILISATIONS. *Cahiers d'histoire mondiale*, 9 (1966), 453-851. [Special issue devoted to encyclopedias] (93JC009) [781]

COLLISON (R.L.W.) Encyclopaedias: their history throughout the ages: a bibliographical guide with extensive historical notes to the general encyclopaedias issued throughout the world from 350 B.C. to the present day. 2nd ed. New York: Hafner, 1966. 334 pp. (00:93) [782]

WALSH (S.P.) Anglo-American general encyclopedias: a historical bibliography, 1703–1967. New York, London: R.R. Bowker Company, 1968. 270 pp. (016:03) [783]

CRAIG (H.) A bibliography of encyclopedias and dictionaries dealing with military, naval and maritime affairs 1577–1971. 4th ed. Houston, Tex.: Department of History, Rice University, 1971. 147 pp. (016:355) [785]

2. English [language]

ENCYCLOPAEDIA PERTHENSIS, or universal dictionary of arts, sciences, literature, *etc.* 2nd ed. Edinburgh: J. Brown, 1816. 23 vol. [786A]

REES (A.), *Ed.* The cyclopaedia; or universal dictionary of the arts, sciences, and literature. London, 1819. 45 vol. (03) [787]

LONDON ENCYCLOPAEDIA, or universal dictionary of science, art, literature, and practical mechanics, comprising a popular view of the present state of knowledge. London: printed for Thomas Tegg, 1829. 22 vol. (03) [788]

EDINBURGH ENCYCLOPAEDIA. London, 1830. 20 vol. (03) [789]

PENNY CYCLOPAEDIA. London, 1833–46. 29 vol. (03) [790]

ENCYCLOPAEDIA METROPOLITANA. 2nd ed. London, 1848–58. 40 vol. (03) [791]

ENGLISH CYCLOPAEDIA. A new dictionary of universal knowledge. London: C. Knight, 1854–70. 22 vol. (03) [791A]

ENCYCLOPAEDIA BRITANNICA. 9th edition. Edinburgh, 1875–88. 25 vol. (03) [792]

ENCYCLOPAEDIA BRITANNICA. 11th edition. Cambridge, 1910–11. 29 vol. (03) [793]

ENCYCLOPAEDIA BRITANNICA. 14th ed. London, 1929. 24 vol. (LPL) [794]

THE NEW ENCYCLOPAEDIA BRITANNICA. 15th ed. Chicago: Encyclopaedia Britannica Inc., 1976. 30 vol. (03) [795]

ENCYCLOPEDIA AMERICANA. New York, 1970. 30 vol. (LPL) [796]

COLLIER'S ENCYCLOPEDIA. With bibliography and index. New York, 1962. 24 vol. (Annual suppl.) [797]

CASSELL'S ENCYCLOPEDIA OF WORLD LITERATURE. New ed. [by] J. Buchanan-Brown. London: Cassell, 1973. 3 vol. [798]

3. Dutch

WINKLER PRINS ENCYCLOPAEDIE. 6 Druk. Amsterdam: Elsevier, 1947–54. 19 vol. [799]

4. French

ENCYCLOPÉDIE OU DICTIONNAIRE RAISONNÉ DES SCIENCES, DES ARTS ET DES MÉTIERS. Mis en ordre par D. Diderot et J. d'Alembert. Paris, 1751–80. 35 vol. (SML) [800]

DESCRIPTION DES ARTS ET MÉTIERS, FAITES OU APPROUVÉES PAR MESSIEURS DE L'ACADÉMIE ROYALE DES SCIENCES. Paris, 1761–89. 76 vol. (SML) [801]

ENCYCLOPÉDIE MÉTHODIQUE. Paris, 1782–1832. 196 vol. (SML) [802]

LA GRANDE ENCYCLOPÉDIE. Sous la direction de M. Berthelot. Paris, 1885–1902. 31 vol. [803]

GRAND LAROUSSE ENCYCLOPÉDIQUE. Paris: Librairie Larousse, 1960–64. 10 vol. (03) [804]

5. German

ZEDLER (J.H.) Grosses vollständiges Universal-Lexikon aller Wissenschaften und Künste. Halle, 1731–1750. 64 vol. [4 suppl. vol., A–Caq] [805]

DEUTSCHE ENCYCLOPÄDIE, ODER, ALLEGEMEINES REAL WÖRTERBUCH ALLER KÜNSTE UND WISSENSCHAFTEN. Frankfurt-on-Main, 1778–1807. 24 vol. [A–Ky. *No more published*] [806]

KRUNITZ (J.G.) Oekonomisch-technologische Enzyclopädie, oder, Allgemeines System der Staats- Stadt- , Haus- und Landwirtschaft. Berlin: Pauli, 1773–1858. 242 vol. [807]

ERSCH (J.S.) *and* GRUBER (J.G.) Allgemeine Encyclopädie der Wissenschaften und Künste. Leipzig: Brockhaus, 1818–89. 167 vol. [A–Phyx. *No more published*] [808]

MEYERS GROSSES KONVERSATIONS-LEXIKON. Leipzig, 1840–55. 46 vol. [809]

MEYERS ENZYKLOPÄDISCHES LEXIKON. Mannheim: Bibliographisches Institut, 1971+ [To be completed in 25 vol.] [810]

DER GROSSE BROCKHAUS. 16. Aufl. Wiesbaden: Brockhaus, 1952–63. 14 vol. [811]

BROCKHAUS ENZYKLOPÄDIE. 17. Aufl. Wiesbaden: Brockhaus, 1966–76. 24 vol. (03) [812]

6. *Italian*

PIVATI (G.F.) Nuovo dizionario scientifico e curioso sacro-profano. Venice, 1746–51. 12 vol. [813]

ENCICLOPEDIA ITALIANA DI SCIENZE, LETTERE ED ARTI. Rome: Treccani, 1929–39. 41 vol. (03) [814]

7. *Russian*

BOL'SHAYA SOVETSKAYA ENTSIKLOPEDIYA. Redaktsiei, N.I. Bukharina, V.V. Kuibysheva [and others]. Moscow, 1926–47. 65 vol. [815]

BOL'SHAYA SOVETSKAYA ENTSIKLOPEDIYA. 2nd ed. Moscow, 1948–58. 53 vol. [3rd ed. (1970+) *in progress*] [816]

GREAT SOVIET ENCYCLOPEDIA. A translation of the 3rd ed. New York: Macmillan, 1973+ (03) [817]

8. *Portuguese*

GRANDE ENCICLOPÉDIA PORTUGESA E BRASILIERA. Lisbon: Ed. Enciclopedia, 1938–58. 37 vol. Apendice, 1958-60. 4 vol. [817A]

9. *Spanish*

ENCICLOPEDIA UNIVERSAL ILUSTRADA EUROPEO-AMERICANA [Espasa]. Madrid: Espasa-Calpe, 1905–33. 80 vol. [Annual suppl.] [818]

XXXVII. PERIODICALS

1. *Abbreviations of Titles*

RUST (W.) Verzeichnis von unklaren Titelkürzungen deutscher und ausländischer Zeitschriften. Leipzig: Harrassowitz, 1927. 142 pp. [819]

LEISTNER (O.) Internationale Titelabkürzungen (ITA) von Zeitschriften, Zeitungen, wichtigen Handbüchern, Wörterbüchern, Gesetzen usw. 2nd ed. Osnabrück: Biblio Verlag, 1970. 1137 pp. [820]

ALKIRE (L.G.) Periodical title abbreviations. 2nd. ed. Detroit, Mich.: Gale Research, 1977. 436 pp. (41.18) [821]

AMERICAN NATIONAL STANDARDS INSTITUTE. *Standards Committee Z 39.* International list of periodical title word abbreviations. Prepared for the UNISIST/ICSU–AB Working Group on Bibliographic Descriptions. Paris: International Council of Scientific Unions, Abstracting Board, 1970. 39 pp. (LPL) [823]

2. *Abstracting Services*

INTERNATIONAL FEDERATION FOR DOCUMENTATION. Abstracting services. Vol. 1. Science and technology. Vol. 2. Social sciences and humanities. The Hague, 1969. (FID publications 455-6) (011/016) [824]

COLLISON (R.L.W.) Abstracts and abstracting services. Santa Barbara, Calif.: ABC Clio, 1971. 122 pp. (011/016) [825]

3. *Bibliographies of Bibliographies*

GUMMER (H.M.) Catalogues and bibliographies of periodicals: a survey of the more important works published in the British Commonwealth and the United States of America since 1945. *Journal of documentation*, 12 (1956), 24-38. (02TL1774) [826]

HAMMOND (M.E.) Catalogues and bibliographies of periodicals: a survey of some foreign guides to periodical literature since 1945. *Journal of documentation*, 14 (1958), 119-135. (02TL1774) [827]

FREITAG (R.S.) Union lists of serials. A bibliography. Washington, D.C.: Library of Congress, 1964. 150 pp. [828]

4. *Guides to Indexes to Periodicals*

HASKELL (D.C.) A check list of cumulative indexes to individual periodicals in the New York Public Library. New York, 1942. 370 pp. (05REF) [829]

KUJOTH (J.S.) Subject guide to periodical indexes and review indexes. Metuchen, N.J.: Scarecrow, 1969. 129 pp. (016:016) [830]

MARCONI (J.V.) Indexed periodicals. A guide to 170 years of coverage in 33 indexing services. Ann Arbor, Mich.: Pierian Pr., 1976. 416 pp. [List of periodical titles identified as being indexed in some 33 American, British and Canadian periodical indexes] (05REF) [831]

5. Indexes to Periodicals

INTERNATIONALE BIBLIOGRAPHIE DER ZEITSCHRIFTENLITERATUR [IBZ]. Osnabrück: Dietrich, 1896+ [Generally known as *IBZ* or *Dietrich*. Currently indexes over 200,000 articles in some 10,000 journals. Covers all fields, but selective. International in scope, but excludes material in Oriental languages. Half-yearly, in three parts: A. List of journals indexed; B. Index by subject; C. Index by author. For an analysis see *Journal of documentation*, 32 (1976), 26-31. Useful for obituaries as it indexes yearbooks of learned societies (Winchell, 687)] [832]

POOLE'S INDEX TO PERIODICAL LITERATURE, 1802–81. Rev. 4th ed. Boston: Houghton, 1891. 2 vol.
————— Supplements. Jan. 1881 – Jan. 1, 1907. Boston, [*c*. 1887–1908]. 5 vol.
————— Cumulative author index, 1802–1906. Compiled by C. Edward Wall. Ann Arbor, Mich.: Pierian Pr., 1971. 488 pp.
[For details *see* Sheehy (687)] [833–835]

POOLE'S INDEX. Date and volume key. By Marion V. Bell and Jean C. Bacon. Chicago: Assn. of College and Reference Libraries, 1957. 61 pp. (ACRL monographs no. 19) [836]

COTGREAVE (A.) A contents subject index to general and periodical literature. Facsimile ed. of 1900 (London). Ann Arbor, Mich.: Gryphon Books, 1971. 744 pp. [837]

MODERN LANGUAGE ASSOCIATION. Victorian periodicals: a guide to research. By Scott Bennett and others. Edited by J. Don Vann and Rosemary T. VanArsdel. New York, 1978. 188 pp. [838]

HOUGHTON (W.E.), *Ed.* The Wellesley index to Victorian periodicals, 1824–1900. Tables of contents and identification of contributors with bibliographies of their articles and stories. Toronto: Univ. of Toronto Pr., 1966–79. 2 vol. (014) [839]

READERS' GUIDE TO PERIODICAL LITERATURE. [Cumulated], 1900+ New York: Wilson, 1905+ [*See* Sheehy (687) for details] [840]

SUBJECT INDEX TO PERIODICALS, 1915–61. London: Library Assn., 1919–62. [*See* Sheehy (687) for details] (016) [841]

ARTS AND HUMANITIES CITATION INDEX 1977+ Philadelphia: Inst. for Scientific Information, 1978+ [841A]

BRITISH HUMANITIES INDEX, 1962+ London: Library Assn., 1963+ [Quarterly. Annual cumulation] [842]

6. *International Bibliographies*

ULRICH'S INTERNATIONAL PERIODICALS DIRECTORY, 1979–1980. A classified guide to current periodicals, foreign and domestic. 18th ed. New York: Bowker, 1979. 2156 pp. (05:011) [843]

WILLING'S EUROPEAN PRESS GUIDE. London: Hutchinson. [Annual published since 1966] (05:011) [844]

7. *National Lists*

TOASE (M.), *Ed.* Guide to current British journals. 2nd ed. by David P. Woodworth. London: Library Assn., 1973. 2 vol. (05:015(410)) [845]

WILLING'S PRESS GUIDE. A guide to the press of the United Kingdom and to the principal publications of Europe and USA. London: Willing, 1871+ [Annual] (05:015(410)) [846]

WEED (K.K.) *and* BOND (R.P.) Studies of British newspapers and periodicals from their beginnings to 1800. A bibliography. Chapel Hill, N.C.: Univ. of North Carolina Pr., 1946. 233 pp. [847]

HATIN (E.) Bibliographie historique et critique de la presse périodique française, ou catalogue systématique et raisonné de tous les écrits périodiques, . . . depuis l'origine du journal jusqu'à nos jours. Paris: Firmin-Didot. 1866. 660 pp. [Chronologically arranged. Notes on some 5,000 journals] [848]

KIRCHNER (J.) Bibliographie der Zeitschriften des deutschen Sprachgebietes bis 1900. Band I: 1670–1870. Stuttgart: Hiersemann, 1966–69. 489 pp. [To be completed in 4 vol.] [849]

BERNARDINI (N.) Guida della stampa periodica italiana. Lecce: Tip. Salentini, 1890. 744 pp. [850]

8. *Union Catalogues*

BRITISH UNION CATALOGUE OF PERIODICALS. A record of the periodicals of the world from the 17th century to the present day, in British libraries. London: Butterworths, 1955–58. 4 vol. Suppl. to 1960. 1962. 1026 pp. (SML) [851] *

BRITISH UNION CATALOGUE OF PERIODICALS, incorporating World List of Scientific Periodicals. New periodical titles, 1960–80. Ed. for the National Central Library by Kenneth I. Porter *and others*. London: Butterworths, 1964–81. [Quarterly. Cumulations 1960–68 and 1969–73 published in 1970 and 1976] (SML) [852] *

UNIVERSITY OF LONDON. *Library*. Union list of serials (ULISES). London, 1977+ [*In progress*. Microfiche] (SML) [853]

UNION LIST OF SERIALS IN LIBRARIES OF THE UNITED STATES AND CANADA. 3rd ed. by E.B. Titus. New York: Wilson, 1965. 5 vol. [1st ed. 1927; 2nd ed. 1943 by W. Gregory. Generally known as *Gregory*. Complete descriptions of some 156,000 serials; changes of title, dates, indexes etc. Gives holdings of 956 U.S. and Canadian libraries. Essential for verifying titles] (SML) [854] *

NEW SERIAL TITLES. A union list of serials commencing publication after December 31, 1949. 1950–1970. Cumulative. Washington: Library of Congress, 1973. 4 vol. Suppl. (SML) [855]

COCKX (A.) Catalogue collectif belge et luxembourgeois des périodiques étrangers en cours de publication. Brussels: Culture et Civilisation, 1965. 2 vol. (05:017.11) [856]

BIBLIOTHÈQUE NATIONALE. *Département des Periodiques*. Catalogue collectif des périodiques du debut du XVIIe siècle à 1939, conservés dans les bibliothèques de Paris et dans les bibliothèques universitaires des départements. Paris, 1967–77. 4 vol. (05:017.11) [857]

DIRECTION DES BIBLIOTHÈQUES ET DE LA LECTURE PUBLIQUE. Inventaire des périodiques étrangers et des publications en série étrangères reçus en France par les bibliothèques et les organismes de documentation en 1965. (Inventaire permanent des périodiques en cours. IPPEC). 4e ed. Paris: Bibliothèque Nationale, 1969. 1207 pp. [858]

BIBLIOTHÈQUE NATIONALE, PARIS. Catalogue collectif des périodiques conservés dans les bibliothèques universitaires de province. Paris, 1943–62. 42 vol. [859]

STAATSBIBLIOTHEK PREUSSISCHER KULTURBESITZ. *Abt. Gesamtkataloge und Dokumentation.* Gesamtverzeichnis deutschsprachiger Zeitschriften und Serien in Bibliotheken der Bundesrepublik einschliesslich Berlin (West). Titel vor 1971 mit Besitznachweisen. Stand: Dezember 1976. (Union list of German language serials in libraries of the Federal Republic of Germany including Berlin (West). Munich: Verlag Dokumentation, 1977. 2 vol. Half-yearly suppl. (05:017.11) [860]

UNIONE INTERNAZIONALE DEGLI ISTITUTI DI ARCHEOLOGIA STORIA E STORIA DELL'ARTE IN ROMA. Catalogo dei periodici esistenti in biblioteche di Roma. Rome, 1975. 986 pp. [861]

9. Library Catalogues

BRITISH MUSEUM. *Department of Printed Books* (*now* British Library). Catalogue of printed books: periodical publications. 2nd ed. London, 1899–1900. 2 vol. (017(410)) [862]

——————— General catalogue of printed books. Vol. 184-186: periodical publications. London, 1963. [For accessions after 1955 *see* supplements to *General catalogue* (954, 955)] (017(410)) [863]

BRITISH LIBRARY. *Lending Division.* Current serials received. April 1981. Boston Spa, 1981. 469 pp. (SML) [864]

UNIVERSITY LIBRARY, CAMBRIDGE. Current serials available in the University Library and in other libraries connected with the University, 1976. Cambridge, 1976. 2 vol. (05:017) [865]

UNIVERSITY LIBRARY, CAMBRIDGE. Classified list of current serials available in the University Library, with an index of subjects 1976. Cambridge, 1977. 619 pp., suppl. (05:017) [866]

UNIVERSITY LIBRARY, CAMBRIDGE. Non-current serials: a select list of holdings in the . . . library. Compiled and edited by B.E. Eaden and M.P. Curtis. Cambridge, 1978. 877 pp. [866A]

ACCADEMIA NAZIONALE DEI LINCEI. *Biblioteca.* I periodici e gli atti accademici italiani dei secoli 17 e 18 posseduti dalla Biblioteca. Catalogo ragionato di Amelia Cosatti. Rome, 1962. 201 pp. (05:017) [867]

10. Newspapers

BRITISH MUSEUM. *Department of Printed Books* (*now* British Library). Catalogue of printed books. Supplement: Newspapers published in Great Britain and Ireland, 1801–1900. London, 1905. 532 col. [Newspapers before 1801 are listed under *Periodical publications* in the *General catalogue* (954). *See also* 868] (017(410)) [867A]

BRITISH LIBRARY. *Newspaper Library.* Catalogue of the Newspaper Library, Colindale. London: British Museum Publns., 1975. 8 vol. (017:07) [868]

WEBBER (R.) World list of national newspapers: a union list of national newspapers in libraries in the British Isles. London: Butterworth, 1976. 95 pp. (07:017) [869]

BODLEIAN LIBRARY, OXFORD. A catalogue of English newspapers and periodicals in the Bodleian Library, 1622–1800. By R.T. Milford and D.M. Sutherland. Oxford: Oxford Bibliographical Society, 1936. 184 pp. [870]

THE TIMES (London). Tercentenary handlist of English and Welsh newspapers, magazines and reviews. London, 1920. 324 pp. [Reprinted 1966] [872]

THE TIMES (London). Palmer's index to The Times newspaper, 1 Oct. 1790 – 30 June 1941. Hampton Wick: Samuel Palmer, 1868–1943. (JT82) [873]

--------- The annual index to The Times 1906–1913. London, 1907–14. 8 vol. [874]

--------- The official index to The Times, 1914+ London, 1914+ [Indexes the final edition] (JT811) [875]

HAGELWEIDE (G.) Deutsche Zeitungsbestände in Bibliotheken und Archiven. Düsseldorf: Droste Verlag, 1974. 372 pp. (Bibliographien zur Geschichte des Parlamentarismus und der politischen Parteien, Heft 6) [876]

NEW YORK TIMES INDEX. Prior series. New York: Bowker, 1966–1973. 9 vol. [When completed (12 vol.) will provide coverage from 1851–1912. Publisher varies] [877]

NEW YORK TIMES INDEX. New York, 1913+ [Annual cumulations] [878]

XXXVIII. SUBJECT INDEXES AND BIBLIOGRAPHIES

1. *Bibliographies of Bibliographies and of Indexes*

TAYLOR (Archer) General subject-indexes since 1548. Philadelphia: Univ. of Pennsylvania Pr., 1966. 336 pp. [879]

GRAY (R.A.) *and* VILLMOW (D.) Serial bibliographies in the humanities and social sciences. Ann Arbor, Mich.: Pierian Pr., 1969. 345 pp. [880]

ROUSE (R.H.) Serial bibliographies for medieval studies. Berkeley: Univ. of California Pr., 1969. 150 pp. (016:94) [881]

2. *Subject Indexes and Bibliographies*

PEDDIE (R.A.) Subject index of books published before 1880. London: Grafton, 1933–48. 4 vol. (017(410)) [882]*

FORTESCUE (G.K.) Subject-index of the modern works added to the library of the British Museum in the years 1880/1885+ London: British Museum, 1886+ [There is a provisional index on microfilm for recent accessions, in the British Library Reading Room] (017(410)) [883]*

PROJECT FOR HISTORICAL BIBLIOGRAPHY, UNIVERSITY OF NEWCASTLE UPON TYNE. Eighteenth-century British books: a subject catalogue. Extracted from the British Museum general catalogue of printed books. London: Dawson, 1979. 4 vol. [Review: *Times Lit. Suppl.*, 11 Dec. 1981, p. 1450] (017(410)) [883A]

LONDON LIBRARY. Subject index of the London Library. By C.T. Hagberg Wright. London, 1909–55. 4 vol. (017(421)) [884]

LIBRARY OF CONGRESS CATALOG. Books: subjects. 1950/54+ Ann Arbor, Mich.: Edwards, 1955+ [Publisher varies] (017(73)) [885]

BRUNET (J.C.) Manuel du libraire et de l'amateur de livres. 5e éd. Paris: Didot, 1860–90. 9 vol. [Vol. 7 and 8: subject indexes] (011) [886]

3. Lists of Titles in Series

BAER (E.A.) Titles in series: a handbook for librarians. 2nd ed. New York: Scarecrow, 1964. 2 vol., suppl. (016:082) [887]

4. Bibliographies of Festschriften

LEISTNER (O.) Internationale Bibliographie der Festschriften. Mit Sachregister. International bibliography of Festschriften. With subject-index. Osnabrück: Biblio Verlag, 1976. 893 pp. [888]

NEW YORK PUBLIC LIBRARY. Guide to *Festschriften*. Vol. 1. The retrospective *Festschriften* collection of the Library: materials catalogued through 1971. Vol. 2. A dictionary catalogue of *Festschriften* in the Library (1972–1976) and the Library of Congress (1968–1976). New York: G.K. Hall, 1977. 2 vol. [889]

5. Bibliographies of Literature, Humanism, etc.

WATT (R.) Bibliotheca britannica; or, A general index to British and foreign literature. Edinburgh: Constable, 1824. 4 vol. (011) [890]

WATSON (George), *Ed.* The new Cambridge bibliography of English literature. Cambridge: Cambridge Univ. Pr., 1974–77. 5 vol. [891]

MODERN HUMANITIES RESEARCH ASSOCIATION. The year's work in modern language studies, 1929/30+ London, 1931+ [Annual] [892]

COSENZA (M.) Biographical and bibliographical dictionary of the Italian humanists and of the world of classical scholarship in Italy, 1300–1800. Boston, Mass.: G.K. Hall, 1962–1967. 6 vol. (VAL) [893]

BIBLIOGRAPHIE INTERNATIONALE DE L'HUMANISME ET DE LA RENAISSANCE. Travaux parus en 1965+ Geneva: Droz, 1966+ (Fédération Internationale des Sociétés et Instituts pour l'Étude de la Renaissance) [Annual] (016:001) [894]

FARRAR (C.P,) *and* EVANS (A.P.) Bibliography of English translations from medieval sources. New York: Columbia Univ. Pr., 1946. 534 pp. (016:8.03) [895]

FERGUSON (M.A.H.) Bibliography of English translations from medieval sources, 1943–1967. New York: Columbia Univ. Pr., 1974. 274 pp. [896]

XXXIX. INFORMATION RETRIEVAL SYSTEMS

[For a survey of major publications on data bases, *see* Sheehy (687), Suppl., pp. 240-246]

HALL (J.L.) *and* BROWN (Marjorie J.) On-line bibliographic data bases. An international directory. 2nd ed. London: Aslib, 1981. 213 pp. [898]

BRITISH LIBRARY. *Research and Development Dept.* Inventory of abstracting and indexing services produced in the UK. By G. Burgess, A. Vickery and S. Keenan. London, 1979. 105 pp. (BL R&D Report 5420) (02TG40786BQ) [899]

LEIGH (J.A.) Guide to computer-based literature searching services in sciences and technology available in the UK. London: Science Reference Library, 1976. 30 pp. (002:681.3) [900]

WILLIAMS (Martha E.) *and* ROUSE (Sandra H.) Computer-readable bibliographic data bases: a directory and data sourcebook. Washington, D.C.: American Society for Information Science, 1976+ (LPL) [901]

THOMAS (Angela) LUCIS guide to computer-based information services. 2nd ed. London: University of London, Central Information Services, 1977. (002:681.3) [902]

XL. LIBRARIES

1. General
2. Directories and Guides to Collections
- *a. International*
- *b. Great Britain*
- *c. Austria*
- *d. France*
- *e. Germany*
- *f. Italy*
- *g. Netherlands*
- *h. Poland*
- *i. Switzerland*
- *j. United States and Canada*
- *k. Yugoslavia*

1. General

BURTON (M.) Famous libraries of the world. London: Grafton, 1937. 458 pp. [903]

ESDAILE (A.) National libraries of the world: their history, administration and public services. 2nd ed. London: Library Assn., 1957. 413 pp. (027) [904]

IRWIN (R.) *and* STAVELEY (R.), *Eds.* The libraries of London. 2nd rev. ed. London: Library Assn., 1964. 332 pp. (017(421)) [905]

2. Directories and Guides to Collections
a. International

WORLD GUIDE TO LIBRARIES. Internationales Bibliotheks-Handbuch. 4th ed. by Helga Langenfelder. New York: Bowker; Pullach (Munich): Verlag Dokumentation, 1974. 2 vol. [906]

STEELE (C.R.) Major libraries of the western world: a selective guide. London and New York: Bowker, 1976. 479 pp. [Practical guide to 300 libraries in 71 countries] (027) [907]

BOALCH (D.H.), *Ed.* World directory of agricultural libraries and documentation centres. Harpenden, Herts.: Internat. Assn. of Agricultural Librarians and Documentalists, 1960. 280 pp. (02REF) [908]

UNITED NATIONS EDUCATIONAL SCIENTIFIC AND CULTURAL ORGANISATION. World guide to technical information and documentation services. Guide mondial des centres de documentation et d'information technique. Paris, 1969. (02REF) [909]

—————— Guide to national bibliographical information centres. Guide des centres nationaux d'information bibliographique. 3rd ed. Paris, 1970. (02REF) [910]

BORN (L.K.) Unpublished bibliographical tools in certain archives and libraries in Europe. Washington, D.C.: Library of Congress, 1952. 25 pp. (017/019) [911]

LEWANSKI (R.C.) Subject collections in European libraries. 2nd ed. London and New York: Bowker, 1978. 495 pp. (02REF) [912]

b. Great Britain

ASSOCIATION OF SPECIAL LIBRARIES AND INFORMATION BUREAUX. The Aslib directory. 4th ed. by Ellen M. Codlin. London, 1977–80. 2 vol. [The 2nd ed. (1957) has a classified index of libraries] (02REF) [913]

LIBRARIES, MUSEUMS AND ART GALLERIES YEARBOOK 1978–79. Edited by Adrian Brink. Cambridge: James Clarke, 1981. [Not paginated] (02REF) [914]

LIBRARY ASSOCIATION. Libraries in the United Kingdom and the Republic of Ireland. 9th ed. London, 1981. 174 pp. (02REF) [915]

BRITISH LIBRARY. *Science Reference Library*. Guide to government department and other libraries and information bureaux. 24th ed. London: 1980. 96 pp. (02REF) [916]

SCOTTISH LIBRARY ASSOCIATION. Library resources in Scotland, 1980–1981. Glasgow, 1981. 149 pp. (02REF) [917]

COLLISON (R.L.W.) Directory of libraries and special collections on Asia and North Africa. London: Crosby, Lockwood and Son, 1970. 123 pp. [918]

WALKER (Gregory) Directory of libraries and special collections on Eastern Europe and the USSR. London: Crosby, Lockwood and Son, 1971. 159 pp. (02REF) [919]

LIBRARY AND ARCHIVE RESOURCES IN THE HISTORY OF SCIENCE. 1. The Turner collection of the history of mathematics at the University of Keele. 2. The Crawford collection of books and manuscripts on the history of astronomy, mathematics, etc., at the Royal Observatory, Edinburgh. 3. The Mathematical Association Library at the University of Leicester. 4. Private manuscript collections in Scotland. 5. History of science in Durham libraries. 6. Manchester. 7. University College London. *British journal for the history of science*, 6 (1972–73), 336-337, 459-461; 7 (1974), 100-103, 201-202; 8 (1975), 94-99; 10 (1977), 89-92; 11 (1978), 191-195. (93JB749) [919A]

LIBRARY ASSOCIATION. *Medical Section.* Directory of medical libraries in the British Isles. 4th ed. London, 1976. 199 pp. (02REF) [920]

OTTLEY (G.) Railway history: a guide to sixty-one collections in libraries and archives in Great Britain. London: Library Assn., 1973. 80 pp. [Complements Ottley's *Bibliography of British railway history* (London: Allen & Unwin, 1965; 683 pp.) (SML)] (016:93:625.1) [921]

TAYLOR (L.J.) *and* TAYLOR (E.A.), *Eds.* Library resources in London and South East England. London: Library Assn., 1979. 275 pp. (02REF) [922]

TOWNSEND (A.C.) *and* STRATTON (G.B.) Library resources in the Greater London area. No. 6, Zoological libraries. London: Library Assn. Reference and Special Libraries Section (South Eastern Group), 1957. 21 pp. (026) [923]

ASSOCIATION OF LONDON CHIEF LIBRARIANS. Directory of London public libraries. 6th ed. by K.R. McColvin. London, 1978. 168 pp. [924]

ROBERTS (Stephen), COOPER (A.) *and* GILDER (L.) Research libraries and collections in the United Kingdom: a selective inventory and guide. London: Clive Bingley, 1978. 285 pp. (02REF) [925]

MORGAN (P.) Oxford libraries outside the Bodleian. 2nd ed. Oxford: Oxford Bibliographical Society, 1980. 264 pp. (02REF) [926]

MUNBY (A.N.L.) Cambridge college libraries: aids for research students. 2nd ed. Cambridge: Heffer, 1962. 56 pp. (027(425.7)) [927]

UNIVERSITY LIBRARY, CAMBRIDGE. Guide to the libraries of the University of Cambridge. Cambridge, 1969. 84 pp. (*Cambridge University Reporter*, vol. 99, no. 29). [College libraries not included] [928]

UNIVERSITY LIBRARY, CAMBRIDGE. Libraries directory, 1979–80. Cambridge, 1979. 20 pp. (*Libraries Information Bulletin*, Suppl. no. 6) (02REF) [929]

c. Austria

VEREINIGUNG ÖSTERREICHISCHER BIBLIOTHEKARE. Handbuch österreichischer Bibliotheken. 1. Bibliotheksverzeichnis. Stand 1970. Vienna: Österreichische Nationalbibliothek, 1971. 394 pp. [930]

d. France
[*See also* 555A]

BIBLIOTHÈQUE NATIONALE, PARIS. Répertoire des bibliothèques et organismes de documentation. Paris, 1971. 733 pp. Supplément 1973. 267 pp. (02REF) [931]

NEWMAN (L.M.) Libraries in Paris: a student's guide. Scorton, Lancs.: Conder Research, 1971. 175 pp. [932]

WELSCH (Erwin K.) Libraries and archives in France. A handbook. Pittsburgh: Council for European Studies, 1973. 78 pp. (02REF) [933]

e. Germany

WELSCH (Erwin K.) Libraries and archives in Germany. Pittsburgh: Council for European Studies, 1975. 275 pp. [934]

VEREIN DEUTSCHER BIBLIOTHEKARE. Jahrbuch der deutschen Bibliotheken. Jahrgang 46. Wiesbaden: Harrassowitz, 1975. 562 pp. [Annual] [935]

DAHME (Klaus) Handbuch der bayerischen Bibliotheken. Wiesbaden: Harrassowitz, 1966. 191 pp. [936]

DEUTSCHE BIBLIOTHEKSKONFERENZ. Deutsche Bibliotheksadressbuch: Verzeichnis von Bibliotheken in der Bundesrepublik Deutschland einschliesslich Berlin (West). 2. Aufl. Berlin: Deutscher Bibliotheksverband, 1976. 498 pp. [937]

GEBHARDT (Walther), *Comp.* Special collections in German libraries: Federal Republic of Germany incl. Berlin (West). Spezialbestände in deutschen Bibliotheken: Bundesrepublik Deutschland einschl. Berlin (West). Berlin: de Gruyter, 1977. 739 pp. (Deutsche Forschungsgemeinschaft) [938]

f. Italy

DIREZIONE GENERALE DELLE ACCADEMIE E BIBLIOTECHE, [ITALY]. Annuario delle biblioteche italiane. 2 ed. Rome: Palombi, 1956–59. 3 vol. [3rd ed. *in progress*. 4 vol. (A–Tor) published 1969–76. (02REF) [939]

LEWANSKI (Rudolf J.) Guide to Italian libraries and archives. Edited by Richard C. Lewanski. New York: Council for European Studies, 1979. 101 pp. [939A]

g. Netherlands

BURKETT (J.) Special libraries and documentation centres in the Netherlands. Oxford: Pergamon, 1968. 103 pp. [940]

h. Poland

LEWANSKI (R.C.) Guide to Polish libraries and archives. Boulder, Colo.: East European Quarterly, 1974. 209 pp. (02REF) [941]

i. Switzerland

VEREINIGUNG SCHWEIZERISCHER BIBLIOTHEKARE Bibliotheken in der Schweiz. Berne, 1976. 192 pp. [942]

j. United States and Canada

KRUZAS (A.T.) Directory of special libraries and information centres. 6th ed. by M.L. Young and H.C. Young. Detroit, Mich.: Gale Research, 1981. 3 vol. (02REF) [943]

AMERICAN LIBRARY DIRECTORY 33rd ed. A classified list of libraries in the United States and Canada. Ed. by Jaques Cattell Press. New York: Bowker, 1980. 1836 pp. (02REF) [944]

ASH (Lee) Subject collections: a guide to special book collections and subject emphases as reported by libraries and museums in the United States and Canada. 5th ed. New York: Bowker, 1978, 1184 pp. (02REF) [945]

NEW YORK PUBLIC LIBRARY. A guide to the reference collections of the New York Public Library. By Karl Brown. New York, 1941. 416 pp. [946]

---------- Guide to the research collections of the New York Public Library. By Sam P. Williams. Chicago: American Library Assn., 1975. 336 pp. (027(747)) [947]

k. Yugoslavia

JOVANOVIĆ (S.) *and* ROJNIĆ (M.) A guide to Yugoslav libraries and archives. Columbus, Ohio: American Assn. for the Advancement of Slavic Studies, 1975. 113 pp. (02REF) [948]

XLI. LIBRARY CATALOGUES

1. *Bibliographies of Catalogues of Libraries*
2. *British Library (*formerly *British Museum, Department of Printed Books)*
3. *Other Libraries in Great Britain*
4. *U.S. Library of Congress*
5. *Bibliothèque Nationale, Paris*

1. *Bibliographies of Catalogues of Libraries*

STEIN (H.) Répertoire des catalogues d'imprimés des principales bibliothèques du monde entier. In: *Manuel de bibliographie générale* (Paris, 1897), Appendice III, pp. 711-768. [*See* 677] (011/016) [948A]

COLLISON (R.L.W.) Published library catalogues: an introduction to their contents and use. London: Mansell, 1973. 184 pp. (017/019) [949]

G.K. HALL & CO. Catalog 1973/1974+ Boston, Mass., 1973+ [Annual trade catalogue. The firm specializes in publishing card catalogues of special libraries] [950]

DOWNS (R.B.) British library resources: a bibliographical guide. Chicago: American Library Assn., 1973. 332 pp. (017/019) [951]

DOWNS (R.B.) *and others*. American library resources: a bibliographical guide. Chicago: American Library Assn., 1951. 428 pp. Suppl. 1950/61, 1961/70. Chicago, 1962–72. 2 vol. [952]

*2. British Library (*formerly *Britsh Museum, Department of Printed Books)*

BRITISH MUSEUM. The catalogues of the British Museum. 1. Printed books. By F.C. Francis. London, 1952. 40 pp. [Originally published in *Journal of documentation*, 4 (1948), (1), 14-40] (02TL1774) [953]

BRITISH MUSEUM. General catalogue of printed books. London, 1960–1966. 263 vol. Ten (Five) year supplement 1956/1965 – 1966/1970. London, 1968, 1971–72. 50 + 26 vol. (017(410)) [954] *

BRITISH LIBRARY. General catalogue of printed books. Five year supplement, 1971–1975. London: British Museum Publications, 1978. 13 vol. (017(410)) [955] *

3. Other Libraries in Great Britain

UNIVERSITY OF LONDON. *Library.* Hand-catalogue of the library. Brought down to the end of 1897. London: HMSO, 1900. 398 pp. [Index of subjects, pp. 355-398] (017(421)) [956]

UNIVERSITY COLLEGE LONDON. *Library.* Catalogue of books in the general library and in the South library. London: Taylor and Francis, 1879. 3 vol. Supplement. London, 1897. (017(421)) [957]

LONDON LIBRARY. Catalogue. By C.T. Hagberg Wright and C.J. Purnell. London, 1913–14. 2 vol. [958]

—––––– —––––– Supplements 1913/20 – 1928/50. London, 1920–53. 3 vol. (017(421)) [959]

BODLEIAN LIBRARY, OXFORD. Catalogus librorum impressorum Bibliothecae Bodleianae . . . Oxford, 1843–51. 4 vol. [960]

UNIVERSITY OF EDINBURGH. *Library*. Catalogue of the printed books. Edinburgh: University Pr., 1918–23. 3 vol. (017(414.4)) [961]

TRINITY COLLEGE DUBLIN. *Library*. Catalogus librorum impressorum qui in Bibliotheca Collegii Sacrosanctae et Individuae Trinitatis, Reginae Elizabethae, juxta Dublin, adservantur. Dublin, 1864–87. 9 vol. [962]

4. United States Library of Congress

LIBRARY OF CONGRESS, WASHINGTON. The National Union Catalog. Pre-1956 imprints. A cumulative author list representing Library of Congress printed cards and titles reported by other American libraries. London: Mansell, 1968–80. 685 vol. (017(73)) [963] *

——————— A catalog of books represented by Library of Congress printed cards, issued to July 31, 1942. Ann Arbor, Mich.: Edwards, 1942–46. 167 vol. Suppl. 1942–1947, 1948–1952. Ann Arbor, Mich.: 1948– 53. 42 + 24 vol. (017(73)) [964–965]

——————— The National Union Catalog: a cumulative author list of works represented by Library of Congress printed cards and titles reported by other American libraries. 1953/1957+ Ann Arbor, Mich.: Edwards, 1958+ [*In progress*. Serves as a continuation of 963] (017(73)) [966]

5. Bibliothèque Nationale, Paris

BIBLIOTHÈQUE NATIONALE, PARIS. Les catalogues du Département des imprimés. Paris, 1970. 54 pp. [*See also* 556] [967]

——————— Catalogue générale des livres imprimés de la Bibliothèque nationale. Auteurs. Paris: 1897+ [Tome 227 (–Wuzel) published in 1977] (017(44)) [968] *

XLII. DIRECTORIES

WORLD OF LEARNING, 1978–79 29th ed. London: Europa Publns., 1978. 2 vol. (058) [969]

MINERVA. Jahrbuch der gelehrten Welt. 1.–30. Jg. Strassburg (Berlin), 1891–1930. [International directory of learned societies and other institutions (Universities, libraries, museums, archives, etc.). After 1914 not published annually. Suspended 1915–1919. Published in separate parts from 31. Jg. (1933/34). For details, *see* Sheehy (687) and Totok (683)] (SML) [970]

MINERVA. Jahrbuch der gelehrten Welt. Abteilung Universitäten und Fachhochschulen. Jg. 31+ Berlin, 1934+ [Suspended 1939–1951] [971]

MINERVA. Jahrbuch der gelehrten Welt. Abteilung Forschungsinstitute, Observatorien, Bibliotheken, Archive, Museen, Kommissionen, Gesellschaften. 31.–32. Jg. Berlin, 1933–37. [972]

MINERVA. Internationales Verzeichnis wissenschaftlicher Institutionen. Forschungsinstitute. 33. Ausgabe (Jahrgang)+ Hrsg. Werner Schuder. Berlin: de Gruyter, 1972+ [973]

INDEX GENERALIS. Annuaire général des universités et des grandes écoles, académies, archives, bibliothèques, instituts scientifiques, musées, centres de recherche, observatoires, sociétés savantes. Paris: Dunod, 1919–55. [21 editions published. Special issue for France published in 1959] (JI18) [974]

INTERNATIONAL DIRECTORY OF ARTS. 15th ed. 1981/82. Frankfurt/Main: Art Address-Verlag Muller, 1981. 2 vol. (084) [975]

NORTON (J.E.) Guide to the national and provincial directories of England and Wales, excluding London, published before 1856. London: Royal Historical Soc., 1950. 241 pp. (017:058) [976]

HARVEY (A.P.) Directory of scientific directories: a world guide to scientific directories including medicine, agriculture, engineering. 2nd ed. London: Francis Hodgson, 1972. 491 pp. (011/016) [977]

HENDERSON (G.P.) Current European directories: annotated guide to international, national, city and specialized directories and similar reference works for all countries of Europe. Beckenham, Kent: CBD Research, 1969. 222 pp. [978]

CURRENT BRITISH DIRECTORIES: a guide to the directories published in Great Britain, Ireland, the British Commonwealth and South Africa. 8th ed. by I.G. Anderson. Beckenham, Kent: CBD Research, 1977. 430 pp. (016:058) [979]

WHITAKER'S ALMANACK. London: Whitaker, 1869+ [Annual] (058) [980]

BINDOFF (S.T.) *and* BOULTON (J.T.) Research in progress in English and history in Britain, Ireland, Canada, Australia, and New Zealand. New ed. London: St. James Press, 1976. 284 pp. [First ed. 1971] [981]

CURRENT BIBLIOGRAPHIC DIRECTORY OF THE ARTS AND SCIENCES (CBD). 1978 annual. An international directory of scientists and scholars. Philadelphia: Inst. for Scientific Information, 1979. 2 vol. (Natural History Museum Library) [981A]

XLIII. DICTIONARIES (Modern Languages)

1. Bibliographies
2. Dictionaries
a. English
b. French

1. Bibliographies

LIBRARY OF CONGRESS, WASHINGTON. Foreign language – English dictionaries. 1. Special subject dictionaries. With emphasis on science and technology. 2. General language dictionaries. Washington, 1955. 2 vol. (016:413) [982]

ZAUNMÜLLER (W.) Bibliographisches Handbuch der Sprachwörterbücher. Ein internationales Verzeichnis von 5600 Wörterbüchern der Jahre 1460–1958 für mehr als 500 Sprachen und Dialekte. Stuttgart: Hiersemann, 1958. 496 col. [983]

WALFORD (A.J.) *and* SCREEN (J.E.O.) Guide to foreign language courses and dictionaries. 3rd ed. London: Library Assn., 1977. 343 pp. (016:413) [984]

COLLISON (R.L.W.) Dictionaries of English and foreign languages. A bibliographical guide to both general and technical dictionaries with historical and explanatory notes and references. 2nd ed. New York, N.Y.: Hafner, 1971. 303 pp. [985]

FACHWÖRTERBÜCHER UND LEXIKA. Ein internationales Verzeichnis. International bibliography of dictionaries. 5. Ausgabe. Munich: Verlag Dokumentation, 1972. 511 pp. (Handbuch der technischen Dokumentation und Bibliographie, Bd. 4) (LPL) [986]

2. *Dictionaries*

a. English

MURRAY (*Sir* James A.H.), *Ed.* New English dictionary on historical principles. Oxford: Clarendon Pr., 1888–1933. [10 vol.; suppl. *in progress*. Described in Sheehy (687)] (413) [987]

——————— Shorter Oxford dictionary on historical principles. 3rd ed. completely reset with etymologies revised by G.W.S. Friedrichsen. Oxford: Clarendon Pr., 1962. 2 vol. (413=2) [988]

ROGET (P.M.) Thesaurus of English words and phrases. New ed. by Robert A. Dutch. London: Longmans, 1962. 1309 pp. (413=2) [989]

WEBSTER'S NEW COLLEGIATE DICTIONARY. [8th ed.] Springfield, Mass.: G.C. Merriam, [1973]. 1536 pp. [990]

BARNHART (C.L.), STEINMETZ (S.) *and* BARNHART (R.K.) The Barnhart dictionary of new English 1963–1972. New York: Clarence Barnhart, Inc., 1973. 512 pp. [991]

b. French

LITTRÉ (E.) Dictionnaire de la langue française. Édition intégrale. Paris: Gallimard, 1958. 7 vol. [First published 1873–83] [992]

ROBERT (Paul) Dictionnaire alphabétique et analogique de la langue française. (Le petit Robert). Paris: Société du Nouveau Littré, 1972. 1971 pp. (413=4) [993]

XLIV. AUTHORSHIP

1. *General*
2. *Presentation of Theses*
3. *English and American Usage*
4. *Copyright*
5. *Style Manuals*
    a. *British Standards*
    b. *Cambridge University Press*
    c. *Oxford University Press*
    d. *HMSO*
    e. *Modern Humanities Research Association*
    f. *Victoria County History*
    g. *Modern Language Association*
    h. *U.S. Government Printing Office*
    i. *University of Chicago Press*
    j. *Others*
6. *Indexing*

1. *General*

[*See also* 303–307]

THE WRITERS' AND ARTISTS' YEARBOOK. A directory for writers, artists, playwrights, writers for film, radio and television, photographers and composers. London: Adam and Charles Black, [Annual] (058) [994]

SCHOLARLY PUBLISHING. A journal for authors and publishers. Toronto, 1969+ [Quarterly] (655JS138) [995]

CALNAN (J.) *and* BARABAS (A.) Writing medical papers: a practical guide. London: Heinemann, 1973. 121 pp. [Practical advice, in a lucid style, much of it relevant to all scholarly writing] [996]

SKILLIN (M. E.) Words into type. Based on studies by Marjorie E. Skillin, Robert M. Gay and other authorities. 3rd ed. Englewood Cliffs, N.J.: Prentice Hall, 1974. 583 pp. [997]

WESTWOOD (John) Typing for print: a manual for typists and authors. London: Pitman, 1976. 66 pp. (001.8) [998]

BUTCHER (Judith) Typescripts, proofs and indexes. Cambridge: University Pr., 1980. 32 pp. (Cambridge authors' and publishers' guides) [998A]

BARRASS (R.) Scientists must write: a guide to better writing for scientists, engineers and students. London: Chapman and Hall, 1978. 176 pp. [999]

EVANS (Hilary) The art of picture research: a guide to current practice, procedure, techniques and resources. Newton Abbot: David and Charles, 1979. 208 pp. (084) [999A]

2. *Presentation of Theses*

BRITISH STANDARDS INSTITUTION. Recommendations for the presentation of theses (BS 4821). London, 1972. 12 pp. [1000]

SUGDEN (V.M.) The graduate thesis. New York: Pitman, 1973. 153 pp. [1001]

TURABIAN (K.L.) A manual for writers of term papers, theses, and dissertations. 4th ed. Chicago: Univ. of Chicago Pr., 1973. 216 pp. (001.8) [1002]

ALLEN (G.R.) The graduate student's guide to theses and dissertations. San Francisco, Calif.: Jossey-Bass, 1973. 108 pp. (001.8) [1003]

HARMAN (E.) *and* MONTAGNES (I.) The thesis and the book. Toronto: Univ. of Toronto Pr., 1976. [Articles culled from *Scholarly publishing*] [1004]

LYON PLAYFAIR LIBRARY, LONDON. Theses and dissertations: tools for writing-up and presentation. 3rd ed. London, 1978. 19 pp. (Outline). [Written for students of Imperial College, London. Gratis] [1005]

3. English and American Usage

GRAVES (Robert) *and* HODGE (Alan) The reader over your shoulder: a handbook for writers of English prose. 2nd ed., abridged. London: Jonathan Cape, 1947. 221 pp. [1006]

WEST (Michael) *and* KIMBER (P.K.) Deskbook of correct English: a dictionary of spelling, punctuation, grammar and usage. London: Longmans, 1957. 191 pp. [1007]

FOWLER (H.W.) A dictionary of modern English usage. 2nd ed. by Sir Ernest Gowers. Oxford: Clarendon Pr., 1968. 725 pp. (413=2) [1008]

PARTRIDGE (Eric) Usage and abusage: a guide to good English. London: Hamish Hamilton, 1970. 392 pp. [Reprint of the 6th ed., 1965] [1009]

REES (Herbert) Rules of printed English. London: Darton, Longman and Todd, 1970. 168 pp. (655.1) [1010]

GOWERS (*Sir* E.A.) The complete plain words. 2nd ed. London: HMSO, 1973. 241 pp. (001) [1011]

CAREY (G.) Mind the stop: a brief guide to punctuation with a note on proof-correction. Rev. ed. Harmondsworth: Penguin, 1976. 126 pp. [Originally published 1958] [1012]

FOLLETT (W.) Modern American usage: a guide. Edited and completed by Jacques Barzun. New York: Hill and Wang, 1966. 436 pp. [1013]

PERRIN (P.G.) Writer's guide and index to English. 5th ed., revised by Wilma R. Ebbitt. Glenview, Ill.: Scott, Foresman, 1972. 765 pp. [1014]

4. Copyright

CAVENDISH (J.M.) A handbook of copyright in British publishing practice. London: Cassell, 1974. 210 pp. (347.77) [1016]

GIBBS-SMITH (C.H.) Copyright law concerning works of art, photographs and the written and spoken word. 2nd ed. London: Museums Assn., 1974. 14 pp. (347.77) [1017]

FLINT (M.F.) A user's guide to copyright. London: Butterworth, 1979. 226 pp. (347.77) [1018]

MILLER (J.K.) Applying the new copyright law: a guide for educators and librarians. Chicago: American Library Assn., 1979. 144 pp. (347.77) [1018A]

SCARLES (Christopher) Copyright. Cambridge: University Pr., 1980. 40 pp. (Cambridge authors' and publishers' guides) [1018B]

5. Style Manuals

a. British Standards

BRITISH STANDARDS INSTITUTION. Guide to copy preparation and proof correction. Part 1: Recommendations for preparation of typescript copy for printing. Part 2: Specification for typographic requirements, marks for copy preparation and proof correction, proofing procedure.

London, 1975–76. 40 pp. (BS 5261) [Part 2 replaces BS 1219: 1958 which is still in wide use in the U.K.] (SML) [1019]

BRITISH STANDARDS INSTITUTION. Recommendations. Bibliographical references. 2nd ed. London, 1976. 11 pp. (BS 1629) [1020]

b. Cambridge University Press

BUTCHER (Judith) Copy-editing: the Cambridge handbook. Cambridge: Cambridge Univ. Pr., 1975. 338 pp. [A comprehensive and practical manual for all those who prepare typescripts and illustrations for printing. 2nd ed. *in press*] (655.1) [1022]

c. Oxford University Press

OXFORD DICTIONARY FOR WRITERS AND EDITORS. Compiled by the Oxford English Dictionary Department. Oxford: Clarendon Pr., 1981. 448 pp. [Successor to eleven editions of F.H. Collins' *Authors' and printers' dictionary* (OUP 1905–73)] (413=2) [1023]

OXFORD UNIVERSITY PRESS. Hart's rules for compositors and readers at the University Press, Oxford. 38th ed., completely revised. Oxford, 1978. 184 pp. [Companion to 1023. "Necessary item in every writer's equipment." Early editions were intended literally *for compositors and readers at the University Press, Oxford.*] (655.1) [1024]

d. Her Majesty's Stationery Office

HER MAJESTY'S STATIONERY OFFICE. Author's guide. London, 1977. 37 pp. [1025]

e. Modern Humanities Research Association

MODERN HUMANITIES RESEARCH ASSOCIATION. MHRA style book. Notes for authors, editors, and writers of dissertations. 3rd ed. by A.S. Maney and R.L. Smallwood. London, 1981. 74 pp. [Includes: guidance on the citation of MSS and of references by the Author-Date system; a table of the new British Standard proof-correction marks] (001.8) [1026]

f. Victoria County History

VICTORIA HISTORY OF THE COUNTIES OF ENGLAND Handbook for editors and authors. Ed. by C.R. Elrington. London: Inst. of Historical Research, 1970. 63 pp. [1027]

g. Modern Language Association

MODERN LANGUAGE ASSOCIATION OF AMERICA. MLA handbook for writers of research papers, theses, and dissertations. New York, 1977. 163 pp. [Supersedes: *The MLA style sheet* (1970)] (001.8) [1028]

h. U.S. Government Printing Office

U.S. GOVERNMENT PRINTING OFFICE. Style manual. Revised ed. Washington, D.C.: 1973. 548 pp. [1029]

i. University of Chicago Press

UNIVERSITY OF CHICAGO PRESS. Manual of style for authors, editors and copywriters. 12th ed., revised. Chicago, 1969. 546 pp. (001.8) [1030]

j. Others

FLEISCHER (E.B.) A style manual for citing microform and nonprint media. Chicago: American Library Assn., 1978. 74 pp. (001.8) [1031]

6. Indexing

SOCIETY OF INDEXERS. A select reading list on indexing. Compiled by Ann Hoffmann. Cambridge, 1978. 30 pp. [Annotated bibliography of 98 items. The Society's official journal, *The Indexer* 1 (1958)– , is devoted to all aspects of indexing] (016:001.815) [1031A]

KNIGHT (G.N.) Indexing, the art of: a guide to the indexing of books and periodicals. London: Allen & Unwin, 1979. 218 pp. (001.8) [1032]

BRITISH STANDARDS INSTITUTION. Recommendations [for] the preparation of indexes to books, periodicals and other publications. London, 1976. 12 pp. (BS 3700) [1033]

ANDERSON (M.D.) Book indexing. Cambridge: University Pr., 1971. 36 pp. (Cambridge authors' and publishers' guides) [1034]

INDEXES

Author/Title index

Subject index

[*The scope and arrangement of the indexes are explained in the Introduction on pages* xii – xiv]

AUTHOR/TITLE INDEX